Records of Achievement

YEAR 6

SCOTTISH PRIMARY 5

Credits

Authors Elaine Hampton and Karen Leigh

Editor Juliet Smith

Assistant Editor Aileen Lalor

Series Designer Rachel O'Kane

Designer Erik Ivens

Cover illustration John-Paul Early

Illustrations Beverley Curl

Published by Scholastic Ltd,
Villiers House,
Clarendon Avenue,
Leamington Spa,
Warwickshire CV32 5PR

Printed by Bell & Bain Ltd, Glasgow

1 2 3 4 5 6 7 8 9 0   4 5 6 7 8 9 0 1 2 3

British Library Cataloguing-in-Publication Data
A catalogue record for this book is available from the British Library.

ISBN 0-439-98365-7

Teachers should consult their own school policies and guidelines concerning practical work and participation of children in scientific experiments. You should only select activities which you feel can be carried out safely and confidently in the classroom.

Contents

Introduction

Assessing a child's progress is a necessary part of school life for children and teachers alike. There are two types of assessment: formal assessment at the end of each key stage (SATs), and teacher assessment, both ongoing and at the end of each key stage. Written reports for parents or carers detailing an individual child's progress and achievements, should be sent home at least once a year.

Reporting and teacher assessment need to be based on evidence, which should be drawn from a child's practical work and from classroom discussion. Records of achievement form another part of this evidence-gathering process, and are an excellent way of checking an individual's level of knowledge.

The *Records of Achievement* series provides photocopiable worksheets that can be integrated with children's own work and your existing scheme of work, adding breadth and variety; or alternatively could be used as the sole record of achievement. By using these worksheets at the end of a topic or unit of study, you can integrate purposeful application of knowledge and skills, differentiation, assessment and record-keeping.

About this book

Curriculum coverage

Each book in the series can be used to provide evidence of progress in the following subject areas:

- science
- history
- geography
- information and communication technology
- art and design
- music
- design and technology
- religious education
- PSHE and citizenship.

English and maths are not included in this series because we feel that most schools already keep comprehensive records in these subjects, including SATs at Year 2 and Year 6, and the optional SATs at Years 3, 4 and 5.

Each activity corresponds to a unit in the QCA Schemes of Work for Year 1. They should therefore be used when a unit of work has been completed. As there is currently no Scheme of Work for PSHE, the content of this section is based on appropriate key areas of study.

Unlike the prescriptive nature of the Schemes of Work for maths and English, teaching other subjects very much depends on how you want to focus particular areas of work. The

Records of Achievement series is relevant to Scottish schools, and those not following the QCA Schemes, as the worksheets relate to the programmes of study most schools would be teaching in any case.

Teacher's notes

There are brief teacher's notes to accompany each activity, providing guidance on the vocabulary the children should have become familiar with in completing the QCA unit, and a brief résumé of what will need to have been studied in order to complete the relevant worksheets.

Differentiated worksheets

There are at least three differentiated worksheets provided for each activity. These are based on the 'end of unit expectations' for the corresponding unit in the QCA Schemes of Work. The level of expectation for each sheet is indicated with ✔ symbols:

✔ for children who have not made so much progress
✔✔ for what most children will have achieved
✔✔✔ for children who have progressed further
✔✔✔✔ for children at the top of the achievement scale.

By differentiating the activities in this way, all children can make an appropriate record of their achievement, regardless of ability, at the end of a unit of study. If appropriate, children could complete more than one worksheet for each activity, depending on their level of knowledge and understanding, as each worksheet builds on the previous one.

The worksheets are designed for children to work on independently. However, the accompanying teacher's notes contain a general introduction to provide a context for the activity before the children begin work. Some children may require support with reading the sheets, but it is important that they work independently to complete the tasks.

Record-keeping

At the bottom of each worksheet is an 'I can...' statement based on the expectations as set out in the relevant QCA unit of study. Once they have completed the sheet satisfactorily, the child can tick the box following the statement; you can then use this information to provide evidence of assessment, and to begin to build up a comprehensive record of an individual's achievements.

Science

Science offers children the opportunity to develop their knowledge and natural curiosity about things they observe and experience. Through the study of science, children can develop a range of skills relating to investigation, analysis and communication. They will also gain respect for living things and an awareness of the importance of health and safety.

In Year 6, the children study the following: 'Interdependence and adaptation' (finding out about what plants need in order to grow, and how animals depend on plants for survival); 'Micro-organisms' (looking at micro-organisms and the diseases they can carry); 'More about dissolving' (extending knowledge and understanding of what happens when a variety of solids dissolve); 'Reversible and irreversible changes' (finding out about melting, freezing, evaporating, condensing, dissolving and burning); 'Balanced and unbalanced forces' (consolidating the learning of forces); 'How we see things' (investigating reflection and shadow formation) and 'Changing circuits' (extending knowledge of electricity and electrical conductors).

Interdependence and adaptation

Unit 6A

✔ **Learning outcome** (page 15)
To understand that green plants need light and water to grow well.

✔✔ **Learning outcome** (page 16)
To know that different animals and plants live in different habitats.

✔✔ **Learning outcome** (page 17)
To recognise that some animals feed on other animals and some on plants.

✔✔ **Learning outcome** (page 18)
To be able to describe how animals are suited to their habitats.

✔✔ **Learning outcome** (page 19)
To understand feeding relationships in a food chain.

✔✔✔ **Learning outcome** (page 20)
To know that green plants are the source of food for all animals and that they produce material for new growth from air, water and the presence of light.

In this unit, the children extend their knowledge of the way in which plants and animals in different habitats depend on each other and are suited to their environment. They will relate feeding relationships to knowledge of plant nutrition. In investigational work, they will focus on making careful observations and measurements, using results to draw conclusions and suggesting explanations for these, using scientific knowledge and understanding.

When working on this unit, make sure the children have become familiar with words and phrases relating to plant growth (*fertiliser, nutrients*); feeding relationships (*consumer, producer, predator, prey, food chain*); and meanings in other contexts (*fertiliser, consumer, producer, key, suited, plant food*).

Photocopiable page 15 requires the children to look at illustrations of a healthy and unhealthy plant and explain the reasons for their appearance. Children completing photocopiable page 16 are required to describe different plants and animals that could be found living in different habitats. For photocopiable page 17, children are asked to list animals that eat other animals and animals that eat plants. Photocopiable page 18 requires the children to describe how animals are suited to their environment. Children completing photocopiable page 19 should be able to draw and label a food chain they have studied and explain the feeding relationships shown within their food chain. For photocopiable page 20, children should be able to order the processes in a food chain and say why a producer is always a green plant.

Micro-organisms
Unit 6B

✔ **Learning outcome** (page 21)
To recognise that very small living things can cause illness.

✔✔ **Learning outcome** (page 22)
To recognise that there are many small organisms which can be used in food production and that these can feed, grow and reproduce.

✔✔✔ **Learning outcome** (page 23)
To give evidence that yeast is living and explain how micro-organisms can move from one food source to another and how this can cause food poisoning.

In this unit, the children will learn that there are many small organisms called micro-organisms, which feed, grow and reproduce and which may be harmful or beneficial. Through experimental and investigative work, they will focus on making observations and drawing conclusions.

When working on this unit, make sure the children have become familiar with words and phrases relating to alternative terms for micro-organisms *(microbe, germ, virus).*

Photocopiable page 21 requires the children to explain what a micro-organism is and describe three ways they could make someone ill. Children are also asked to identify how to reduce the chances of passing illness on to someone, for example washing hands, covering nose and mouth when coughing and sneezing. Children completing photocopiable page 22 are required to describe three different micro-organisms, where they are found and what they might do. They are also required to explain how a micro-organism can be used in food production. For photocopiable page 23, the children should be able to identify that yeast is present in both bread and beer and to explain what it does. They should also be able to list some other micro-organisms used in food production and how these micro-organisms can be a danger to the consumer.

More about dissolving
Unit 6C

✔ Learning outcome (page 24)
To recognise that a solid can be recovered from a solution by evaporation.

✔✔ Learning outcome (page 25)
To investigate aspects of dissolving and present results in a table.

✔✔✔ Learning outcome (page 26)
To understand that solids remain in the solution when they dissolve and that they can be recovered by evaporation.
To recognise that there is a limit to how much solid will dissolve in a liquid.

✔✔✔ Learning outcome (page 27)
To identify several factors that affect the rate at which a solid will dissolve.

✔✔✔✔ Learning outcome (page 28)
To present results in a line graph and explain why it is important to repeat measurements.

In this unit, the children will extend their knowledge of what happens when a variety of solids dissolve. Experimental and investigative work focuses on making and testing predictions; planning a fair test; repeating observations and measurements; representing data in line graphs and interpreting what these show. Work on this unit also offers opportunities for relating the understanding of dissolving to everyday contexts.

When working on this unit, make sure that the children have become familiar with words and phrases relating to separating mixtures *(dissolved, undissolved, solution, mixture, evaporate, condense, pure)* and data handling *(bar line graph, line graph, average, accurate).*

Photocopiable page 24 requires the children to circle items that can be dissolved and describe how something that has dissolved can be recovered from the solution. For photocopiable page 25, children are expected to describe something they have dissolved and record the results of an aspect of dissolving that they have researched. Children completing photocopiable page 26 should be able to describe the processes of dissolving and evaporation. They should also be able to describe an investigation they could carry out to show that there is a limit to how much salt will dissolve in water. Photocopiable page 27 poses the question: 'Do all solids dissolve at the same rate?' and children are expected to list three factors that affect the rate at which solids dissolve. For photocopiable page 28, children should have carried out an investigation to find out whether the statement 'all solids dissolve at the same rate' is true and should be able record their results on a line graph. They are also required to explain the importance of repeating measurements and of drawing a conclusion.

Reversible and irreversible changes

Unit 6D

✓ **Learning outcome** (page 29)
To describe changes and to state whether they are reversible or irreversible.

✓✓ **Learning outcome** (page 30)
To describe and classify changes and recognise that irreversible changes often make new and useful materials.

✓✓✓ **Learning outcome** (page 31)
To recognise the hazards of burning materials.

✓✓✓✓ **Learning outcome** (page 32)
To understand that in some cases the new materials made when burning can be gases and identify some evidence for this.

In this unit, the children will consolidate work they have previously done on reversible changes, for example melting, freezing, evaporating, dissolving and condensing. The unit introduces burning as a change that cannot be reversed and, like other irreversible changes, produces new materials. Experimental and investigative work focuses on making careful observations, using scientific knowledge and understanding, and suggesting explanations for observations.

When working on this unit make sure the children have become familiar with words and phrases relating to changes *(reversible, irreversible).*

Photocopiable page 29 requires the children to group some materials into those which dissolve in water, those which don't dissolve and those where there appears to be a different change. They are also required to describe the processes they used in changing a material and changing it back again. Children completing photocopiable page 30 should be able to describe what happens when ice and a raw egg are heated and whether the changes are reversible or irreversible. They should also be able to write about two useful materials that can be formed from an irreversible change. Photocopiable page 31 asks the children to describe what happens when a material is burnt and to explain the hazards of burning materials. For photocopiable page 32 the children are expected to answer some questions relating to the gas that is formed when something is burnt and how this can be proved.

Balanced and unbalanced forces

Unit 6E

✔ Learning outcome (page 33)
To identify weight as a force and understand that more than one force can act on an object.

✔✔ Learning outcome (page 34)
To identify weight as a force that is measured in newtons. To be able to describe some situations when two forces may be acting on an object and recognise that when an object is at rest the forces are balanced.

✔✔✔ Learning outcome (page 35)
To describe and explain the motion of some familiar objects in terms of balanced or unbalanced forces.

In this unit, the children will apply their knowledge of a variety of forces, including magnetic attraction, gravity and friction, to contexts in which objects are stationary because forces on them are balanced. Children will learn about the changes in motion that can occur when forces are not balanced. They will also consolidate their understanding that forces have direction and can be measured. Experimental and investigative work will focus on making and repeating measurements, considering patterns in results, representing data on line graphs, and using results to draw conclusions.

When working on this unit make sure the children have become familiar with words and phrases relating to forces and the measurement of forces *(weight, gravity, upthrust, balance, newton, force meter.)* They should begin to have an understanding of near synonyms like *still, stationary, at rest, not moving.*

Photocopiable page 33 requires the children to explain what happens to make a ball come down when it is thrown in the air and to describe how it might feel to walk on the moon. Children completing photocopiable page 34 should be able to record an investigation they have carried out using newtons to measure a force, including what they were finding out and what their conclusion was. They should also be able to describe two different situations when two forces are acting on an object. For photocopiable page 35 children are expected to use arrows to portray the forces acting on a toy vehicle when it is on a level board and to do the same when it is on a sloping board.

How we see things

Unit 6F

✔ **Learning outcome** (page 36)
To recognise that when light is blocked a shadow is formed. To understand that reflections can be seen in shiny surfaces.

✔✔ **Learning outcome** (page 37)
To understand that light travels from a source and that when it is blocked a shadow is made and that when it hits a shiny surface it is reflected. To understand that light sources are seen when light from them enters the eye.

✔✔✔ **Learning outcome** (page 38)
To explain the differences between shadow formation and reflection in terms of the path of light.

In this unit, the children will learn that mirrors and shiny surfaces alter the direction in which light travels and that when they see objects, light enters the eye. They will contrast reflection and shadow formation. Experimental and investigational work will focus on: planning and carrying out a fair test; making observations and measurements; recognising when to repeat measurements; presenting results in line graphs and identifying patterns in data.

When working on this unit, make sure the children have become familiar with words and phrases relating to shadow formation and reflection *(opaque, reflect, reflection, light beam, mirror, light travelling)*.

Photocopiable page 36 requires the children to explain what is happening in an illustration of a torch shining on a shape and why the shadow is formed. They are also required to explain how the size or shape of the shadow could be changed, for example by moving the light source or the object. Children completing photocopiable page 37 are asked to look at an illustration and draw a line to show where the shadow of a tree would be with the sun shining on it. They are then expected to explain what happens when you look in a mirror and why, and explain the process that allows you to see lights twinkling on a Christmas tree. Photocopiable page 38 requires the children to draw their own shadow and reflection and explain the differences between them.

Changing circuits
Unit 6G

✔ **Learning outcome** (page 39)
To recognise conventional symbols for some electrical components and construct a working circuit with specified components.

✔✔ **Learning outcome** (page 40)
To understand how to change the brightness of a bulb in a circuit. To draw circuit diagrams and construct circuits from diagrams using conventional symbols.

✔✔✔ **Learning outcome** (page 41)
To be able to interpret more complex circuit diagrams and describe the differences between wires usually used for circuits and fuse wires.

In this unit, the children will consolidate knowledge of materials that are electrical conductors and extend understanding of ways in which the brightness of a bulb or speed of motors in a circuit can be changed. They will also develop their understanding of the value of using conventional symbols for communication. This unit provides them with the opportunity to carry out a complete investigation relating to circuits.

When working on this unit, make sure the children have become familiar with words and phrases relating to electrical circuits *(complete circuit, conductor, insulator, circuit symbol, component, circuit diagram, cell).*

Photocopiable page 39 requires the children to look at a diagram using conventional symbols and draw the working circuit it portrays. Children completing photocopiable page 40 should be able to draw an illustration to show how to increase the brightness of a bulb in a circuit. They should also be able to draw a circuit diagram using the symbols for some listed components. For photocopiable page 41 the children are asked to answer some questions about a real life circuit. They are also asked to explain why wires are usually covered with plastic and when it is safe to use bare wires.

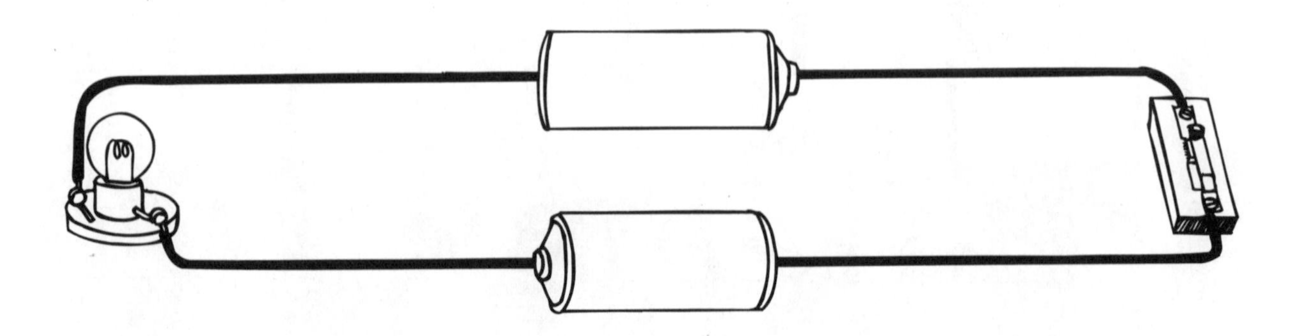

Name ______________________________ Date ____________________

Interdependence and adaptation

- Look at the two illustrations above and describe the conditions the two plants have been kept in to make them look this way.

____

____

- What are the main things a plant needs to grow well?

____

____

- Why do plants need light?

____

____

- Why do plants need water?

____

____

I can recognise that a green plant needs light and water to grow well. ☐

Name ______________________________ Date __________________

Interdependence and adaptation

- You will have previously studied local habitats. Describe some of the different plants and animals that could be found living in these habitats.

A garden	A forest

A field	A school playground

I can recognise that different animals and plants live in different habitats. ☐

Name ______________________ Date ______________

Interdependence and adaptation

- Animals and plants living in the same habitat depend on each other. Some animals eat other animals and some eat plants. Using your own observations of local habitats, complete the following table:

Animals that eat other animals	Animals that eat plants

I can recognise that some animals feed on other animals and some on plants. ☐

Name ______________________ Date ______________

Interdependence and adaptation

- Choose two animals you have found out about that live in different locations.

- Describe how they are suited to the conditions found there.

1. ____

____

2. ____

____

- How are the following plants and animals suited to their habitats?

A cactus

____

____

____

____

____

____

A polar bear

____

____

____

____

____

____

I can describe how animals are suited to the conditions found in their habitats. ☐

Name ______________________________ Date ___________________

Interdependence and adaptation

- Draw a food chain you have studied and label it.

- Describe your food chain in words, describing the feeding relationships between the animals and/or plants.

____

____

____

____

I can represent feeding relationships in a food chain. ☐

Name ______________________ Date ______________

Interdependence and adaptation

- Put these words describing a food chain into the correct order.

primary consumer   tertiary consumer

producer   secondary consumer

- What will the producer always be and why?

____

____

- Draw a food chain you have studied.

- Explain the process that makes a producer able to do the job.

____

____

I can recognise that green plants are the source of food for all animals and that they produce material for new growth from air, water and light. ☐

Name ______________________ Date ______________

Micro-organisms

- What is a micro-organism?

____

____

____

- Describe three ways that they can make someone ill.

____

____

____

____

____

____

- How could you reduce the chances of passing on an illness to someone else?

____

____

____

____

____

____

____

____

Record of Achievement

I can recognise that very small living things can cause illness. ☐

Name ______________________ Date ______________

Micro-organisms

- Describe these three different micro-organisms. Include where they are found and what they do.

Bacteria

____

____

____

Fungi

____

____

____

Viruses

____

____

____

- Explain how a micro-organism can be used in food production.

____

____

____

____

Record of Achievement

I can recognise that there are many small organisms which can cause illness or decay or which can be used in food production and that these micro organisms feed, grow and reproduce. ☐

Name ______________________________ Date ____________________

Micro-organisms

- What do these two items have in common?

____

- Explain what yeast does.

____

____

- List some other micro-organisms used in food production.

____

____

- How can these micro-organisms be a danger to the consumer?

____

____

____

I can describe evidence that yeast is living and explain how micro-organisms can move from one food source to another and how this can cause food poisoning. ☐

Name ______________________ Date ______________

More about dissolving

- Put a ring around the items that can be dissolved.

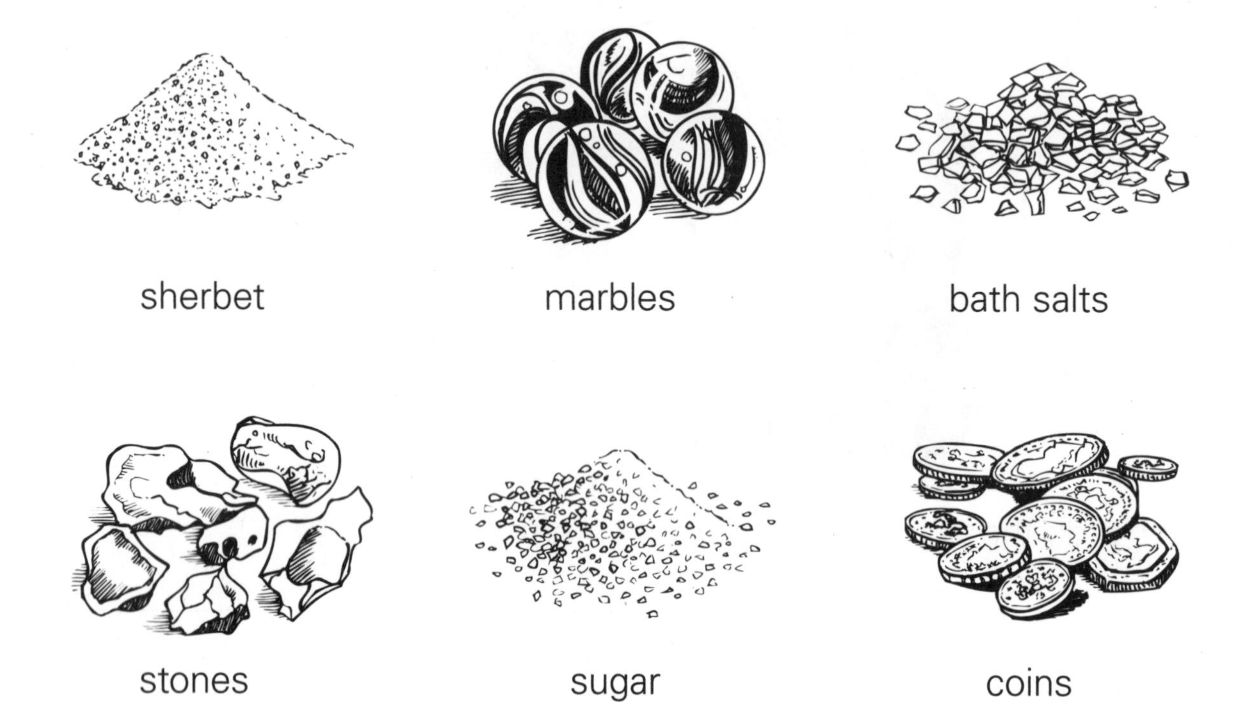

- Describe how something that has dissolved can be recovered from the solution.

____

____

____

____

____

____

____

I can recognise that a solid can be recovered from a solution by evaporation. ☐

Name ______________________________ Date __________________

More about dissolving

- Describe something you have dissolved.

____

____

- Choose an aspect of dissolving that you have researched and record your results in a table. Draw or stick your table in the space below.

I can investigate an aspect of dissolving and present results in a table. ☐

Name ______________________________ Date ____________________

More about dissolving

- Describe the following processes.

Dissolving

____

____

____

____

Evaporation

____

____

____

____

- Describe an investigation you could carry out to show that there is a limit to how much salt will dissolve in water.

____

____

____

____

____

____

____

I recognise that solids remain in the solution when they dissolve and can be recovered by evaporation. I recognise that there is a limit to how much solid will dissolve. ☐

Name ______________________________ Date ________________

More about dissolving

- Will all solids dissolve at the same rate?

____

____

- Explain your answer.

____

____

____

____

____

____

____

____

- List three factors that will affect the rate at which solids dissolve.

1. ______________________________

____

2. ______________________________

____

3. ______________________________

____

I can identify several factors that will affect the rate at which solids dissolve. ☐

Name ______________________ Date ______________

More about dissolving

- Using a range of solids, plan an investigation to see if the above statement is true. Record your results on a line graph and stick a copy of the graph in the space below.

- What is your conclusion?

- Explain why it is important to repeat measurements.

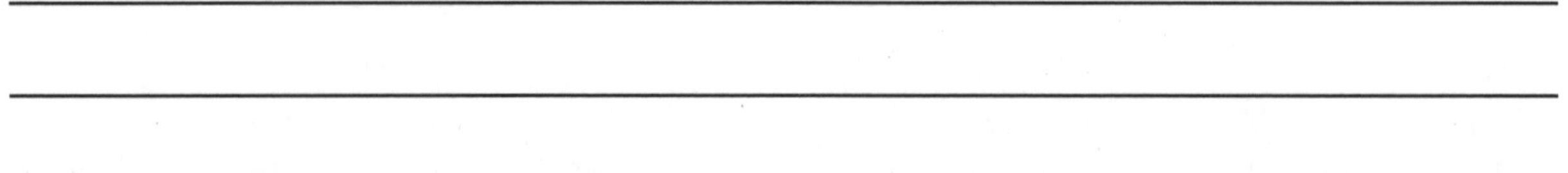

I can present results in a line graph and explain why it is important to repeat measurements. ☐

Name ______________________ Date ______________

Reversible and irreversible changes

- List some materials in the following groups.

Those which dissolve in water

____

____

____

Those which won't dissolve in water

____

____

____

Those where there appears to be a different change

____

____

____

- Describe how you changed a material and then changed it back.

____

____

____

- Describe how you made a change to a material that was irreversible.

____

____

____

I can describe a number of changes and identify whether some changes are irreversible or not. ☐

Name ______________________ Date ______________

Reversible and irreversible changes

- Describe what happens when ice is heated.

____

____

- Is this change reversible or irreversible?

____

____

- What happens when a raw egg is heated?

____

____

Is this change reversible or irreversible?

____

____

- What is an irreversible change?

____

____

- Write about two useful materials that can be formed from an irreversible change.

____

____

____

____

Record of Achievement

I can describe a number of changes and classify them.
I can recognise that irreversible changes often make new and useful materials. ☐

Name ______________________________ Date __________________

Reversible and irreversible changes

- Choose a material you have burned in class. Write its name here:

____

- Describe what you observed.

____
____
____
____
____
____
____

- Think of some other materials and explain some of the hazards of burning them. Also consider how to minimise those hazards.

____
____
____
____
____
____
____
____
____
____

Record of Achievement

I can recognise the hazards of burning materials. ☐

Name ______________________________ Date ____________________

Reversible and irreversible changes

- Answer the following questions.

What is a fuel?

____

____

____

____

What other materials can be formed when something burns?

____

____

How could you show if an invisible gas is formed?

____

____

____

____

____

____

____

____

____

____

I can explain that in some cases the new materials made are gases and identify some evidence for the production of gases. ☐

Name ______________________ Date ______________

Balanced and unbalanced forces

- Look at the picture. When the boy throws the ball in the air what makes it come down?

____

____

____

____

- Describe what it would feel like to walk on the Moon and why.

____

____

- Look at the picture above. What is happening to keep the boat afloat?

____

____

I can identify weight as a force and that more than one force can act on an object. ☐

Name ______________________ Date ______________

Balanced and unbalanced forces

- In the space below, record or stick an investigation you have carried out using newtons to measure a force.

What were you finding out?

____

What was your conclusion?

____

____

- Describe two different situations where two forces are acting on an object.

____

____

- Look at this picture. What is happening here?

____

____

____

I can identify that weight is a force and it is measured in newtons. I can describe some situations in which there are two forces acting on an object and recognise that when an object is at rest the forces are balanced. ☐

Name ______________________________ Date ____________________

Balanced and unbalanced forces

- Draw arrows on the picture below to show the forces acting on the vehicle.

- Explain what is happening.

____

____

____

- Draw arrows on the picture below to show the forces acting on the vehicle.

- Explain what is happening and why.

____

____

____

I can describe and explain the motion of some familiar objects in terms of balanced and unbalanced forces. ☐

Name ______________________________ Date ____________________

How we see things

- Explain what is happening in the above illustration.

____

____

- Describe how you could change the size or shape of the shadow.

____

____

- Make a list of some things you can see your reflection in.

____

____

- Explain how this happens.

____

____

I can recognise that when light is blocked, a shadow is formed and that reflections can be seen in shiny surfaces. ☐

Name ______________________ Date ______________

How we see things

- In the picture below, draw an outline to show where the shadow of the tree would be.

- Why is the shadow formed?

____

____

- What happens when you look in a mirror and why?

____

____

- Explain what enables you to see Christmas lights.

____

____

____

____

____

____

Record of Achievement

I can recognise that light travels from a source and that when it is blocked a shadow is made and that when it hits a shiny surface it is reflected. I can recognise that light sources are seen when light from them enters the eye. ☐

Name ______________________________ Date ____________________

How we see things

- Draw your shadow.
- Draw your reflection

- What are the differences?

____

____

____

- Why does this happen?

____

____

____

Record of Achievement

I can explain the difference between shadow formation and reflection in terms of the path of light. ☐

Name ______________________________ Date ____________________

Changing circuits

- Look at this diagram, which uses conventional symbols for electrical components. In the space below, draw the working circuit it portrays.

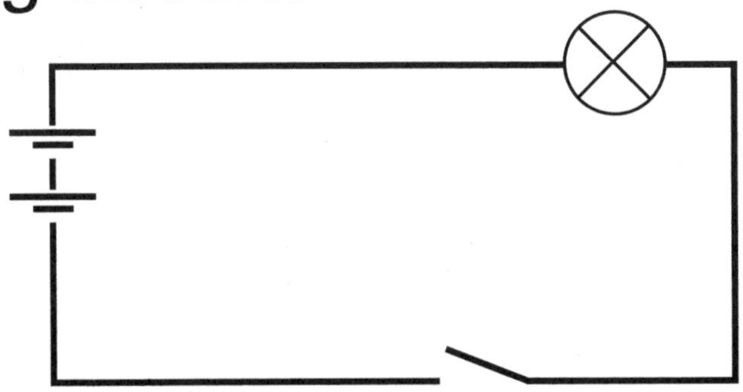

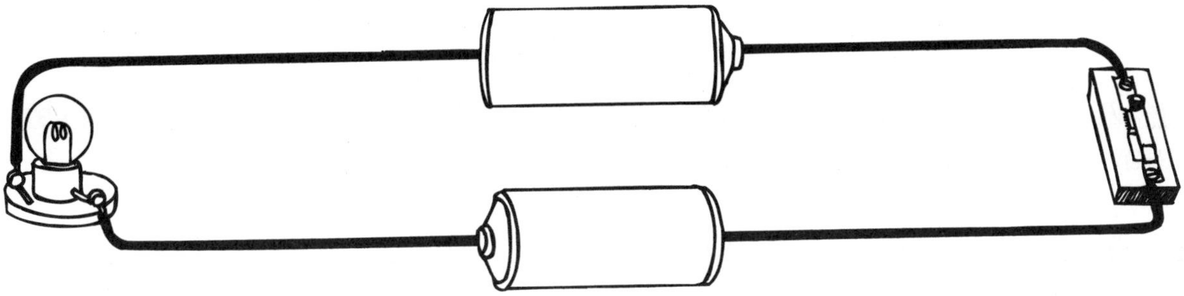

- In the space below copy the circuit shown above, using the correct symbols.

Record of Achievement

I can recognise conventional symbols for some electrical components and construct a working circuit with specified components. ☐

Name ______________________ Date ________________

Changing circuits

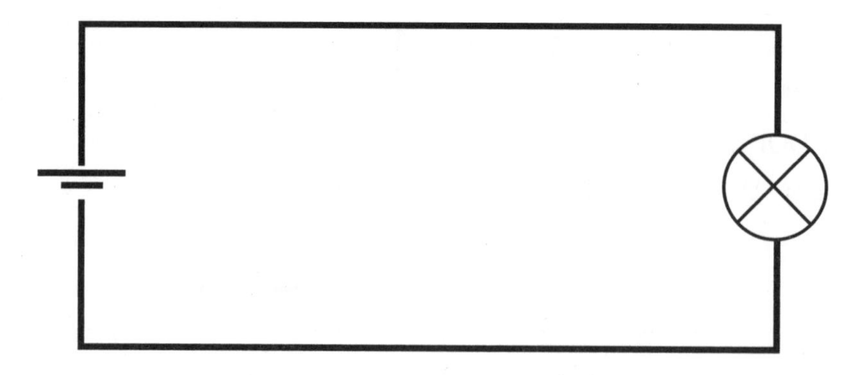

- Draw two illustrations showing how to increase the light coming from the bulb shown in the circuit above.

- Draw a circuit diagram using the conventional symbols for items listed below.

a buzzer **wires** **two bulbs** **two batteries** **a motor**

I can suggest ways of changing the brightness of a bulb, draw circuit diagrams and construct circuits from diagrams using conventional symbols. ☐

Name ______________________ Date ______________

Changing circuits

Time-delay switch

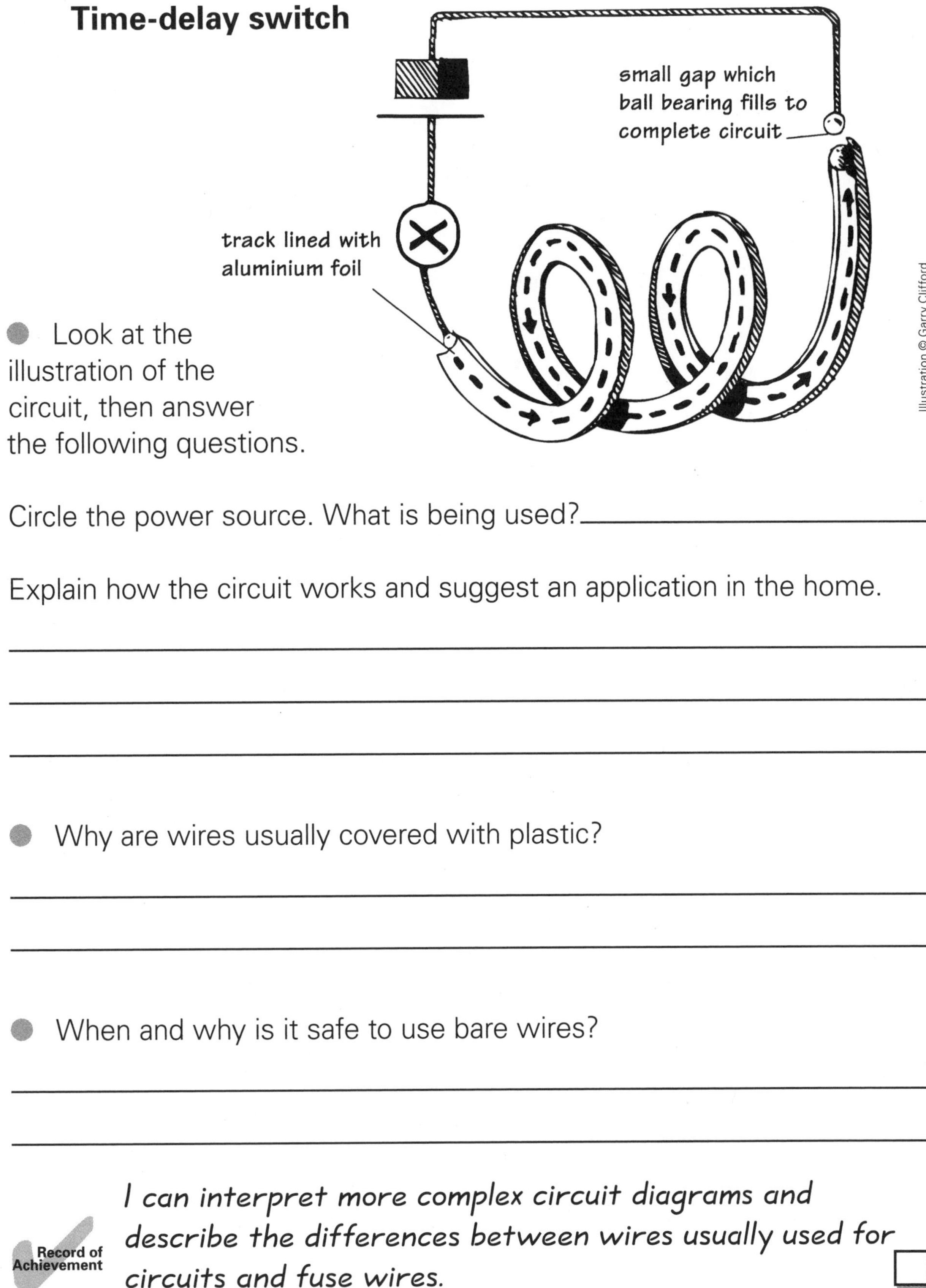

- Look at the illustration of the circuit, then answer the following questions.

Circle the power source. What is being used? ______________

Explain how the circuit works and suggest an application in the home.

____

____

____

- Why are wires usually covered with plastic?

____

____

- When and why is it safe to use bare wires?

____

____

Record of Achievement

I can interpret more complex circuit diagrams and describe the differences between wires usually used for circuits and fuse wires. ☐

History

History provides children with the opportunity to develop their understanding of how and why we interpret the past, how people lived in the past and how modern-day lives can be affected by past events. Children should be given plenty of opportunity to study events from the past, how and why they happened and what the events resulted in.

In Year 6, the children find out about: changes to their locality in Victorian times; changes that have taken place in Britain since 1948 and how aspects of life from Ancient Greece are still relevant today.

How did life change in our locality in Victorian times?

Unit 12

✔ **Learning outcome** (page 46)
To describe some features of the period.

✔✔ **Learning outcome** (page 47)
To make appropriate use of dates.
To identify changes in the locality within the Victorian period and give reasons for the changes.

✔✔✔ **Learning outcome** (page 48)
To describe and explain the results of some of the main events and changes in the locality.

In this unit, children investigate some of the ways their local area changed during the Victorian era, and discover some of the reasons for these changes. Children will use the local area to explore characteristic features of Victorian times, look at how the area has changed over time and find the reasons for (and results of) these changes. Children should develop their sense of chronology from buildings and other information sources, and learn to ask and answer questions.

When working on this unit, make sure that the children have become familiar with words and phrases relating to: local history studies *(census, trade directory, street directory, locality); Victorian housing (villa, terraced house, tied cottage, workhouse, sash window, bargeboards, gable)* and industrialisation *(mechanisation, urbanisation, public health).*

Photocopiable page 46 requires the children to find the correct endings for some sentences about life in Victorian times and to describe how steam engines altered the life of people. Photocopiable page 47 requires the children to put some dates from the Victorian period on a timeline and choose to write about two things that changed in the Victorian period in their locality. Photocopiable 48 requires the children to write about changes in their area in the Victorian period

● History

How has life has in Britain changed since 1948?

Unit 13

✔ **Learning outcome** (page 49)
To understand about some aspects of British life since 1948. To identify some similarities and differences between 1948 and today.

✔✔ **Learning outcome** (page 50)
To identify and give reasons for some of the changes since 1948.

✔✔✔ **Learning outcome** (page 51)
To make links between the changes and the causes of the changes in British life since 1948.

In this unit, children learn about the reasons for and results of the changes in British life since 1948. Children investigate in depth one aspect of change in British life, for example, population structure, popular culture, or work. They will develop their historical understanding of the period, including the characteristic features and diversity of popular culture. They will make links between changes both within and across the period, and apply their skills of historical enquiry to a study of the recent past.

When working on this unit, make sure that the children have become familiar with words and phrases relating to settlement *(population, emigration, immigration);* aspects of society *(industry, work, leisure, transport, media, fashion, diet)* and change *(different, same as, because, cause, effect, reasons, results).*

Photocopiable page 49 requires the children to identify things people would have in their houses in 1948 and list the things we still have today. Children completing photocopiable page 50 are required to look at different sources of information, including a population graph, a table of consumer goods found in living rooms in 1948 and 2003, and a life expectancy graph. The children are then asked to use the information to identify how life has changed since 1948, and give reasons for the changes. For photocopiable page 51 children are expected to make links between the changes and the causes of the changes of some aspects of everyday life.

History

How do we use Ancient Greek ideas today?

Unit 15

✔ **Learning outcome** (page 52)
To know some aspects of the life of the Ancient Greeks.

✔✔ **Learning outcome** (page 53)
To know that the Ancient Greeks have influenced school life today.

✔✔✔ **Learning outcome** (page 54)
To know the ways the Ancient Greeks influenced life today. To give reasons why life today and life in Ancient Greece are similar in some ways.

✔✔✔ **Learning outcome** (page 55)
To compare and contrast the ancient and modern versions of the Olympic games,

In this unit, the children use their own experience, particularly of being at school, as a springboard to find out about the influence that the Ancient Greeks continue to have on our lives. They should use a wide range of sources, including archaeology, to find out about the Ancient Greeks and compare a past society with society today.

When working on this unit, make sure that the children have become familiar with words and phrases relating to Ancient Greece (*legacy, civilisation, alphabet, technology, history, geography, telephone, sculpture, column, frieze, capital*).

Photocopiable page 52 requires the children to complete a cloze procedure about the life of the Ancient Greeks. Children completing photocopiable page 53 are asked to write a list of the subjects they study in school today and then compare this with a list of subjects children would have studied in Ancient Greece. They are then asked to describe how an aspect of life in Ancient Greece differs from life today. For photocopiable page 54, children are expected to identify four things we do today that the Ancient Greeks did and why we continue to do these things. They are also asked to make comparisons between modern-day and Ancient Greek drama, politics and architecture. Finally, photocopiable page 55 asks the children to describe the similarities and differences between the ancient and modern Olympic games.

Name ______________________________ Date ____________________

How did life change in our locality in Victorian times?

- For each of the following sentences, match each beginning with the correct ending.

Houses were made from	go to school
By 1900 all children would	most important fuel
Trains meant that	ships, factories and trains
People would work in	bricks and slate
Steam engines would be used in	people could travel further
Coal was the	factories

- How did steam engines affect people's lives?

____

____

____

I can describe some features of the period. ☐

Name ______________________________ Date ____________________

How did life change in our locality in Victorian times?

- Draw lines to put these facts and dates on the timeline.

Victoria dies 1901 | Victoria becomes queen 1837 | Great exhibition 1852

1800 1810 1820 1830 1840 1850 1860 1870 1890 1900 1910

- Choose one thing from the list below. Circle it and then describe how it changed in your locality during the Victorian period.

medicine

how people worked

education of the poor

housing

transport

____

____

____

____

____

____

Record of Achievement

I can make appropriate use of dates. I can identify changes in my locality within the Victorian period and give reasons for the changes. ☐

Name ______________________________ Date ____________________

How did life change in our locality in Victorian times?

- There would have been many changes in your area during the Victorian period. Describe these changes (try to mention houses, transport, jobs and education).

I can find out about the past in my locality and describe the changes. ☐

Name ______________________ Date ______________

How has life changed in Britain since 1948?

- In the list below, underline the things that most people would have had in their houses in 1948.

television

radio

video recorder

fridge

cooker

microwave

coal fire

hi-fi

DVD player

pantry

outside toilet

piped hot water

- Write down some of the things from the list that most people still have today.

I know some aspects of British life since 1948. I can identify some similarities and differences between 1948 and today. ☐

Name ______________________ Date ______________

How has life changed in Britain since 1948?

- The sources below show specific changes since 1948. Describe the changes each source shows. Then give reasons why these changes have occurred.

Source 1

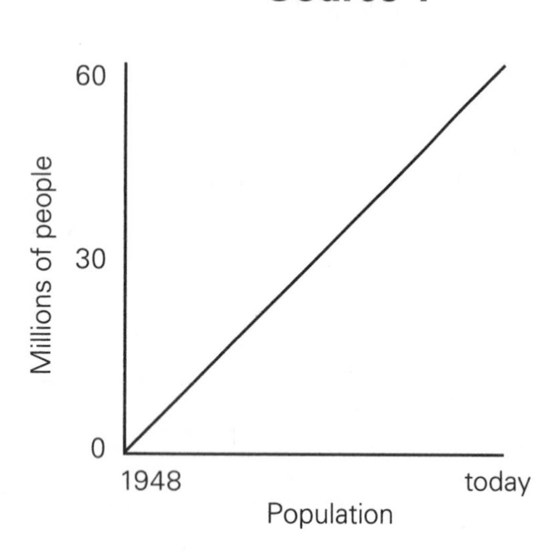

____

____

____

____

Source 2

Consumer goods in a 1948 living room	Consumer goods in a 2004 living room
Radio	Hi-fi
Gramophone	DVD player
	Video recorder
	Colour television

____

____

____

____

Source 3

100
50
0
Life Expectancy
1948
2000
Years

____

____

____

____

Record of Achievement

I understand about aspects of British life since 1948. I can identify and give reasons for the changes. ☐

Name ______________________ Date ______________

How has life changed in Britain since 1948?

- Below are two boxes. Draw a line from the things in the 'Then' box to their consequences in the 'Now' box.

Then	Now
National Health Service	Growth of factories making consumer goods
More wages	Growth of the holiday industry
More free time	More roads and motorways
Cheaper cars	Higher life expectancy

- Describe in detail how some things have changed since 1948.

____

____

____

____

____

____

____

____

____

____

I can make links between the changes and the causes of the changes in British life since 1948. ☐

Name ______________________ Date ______________

How do we use Ancient Greek ideas today?

- Use the words in the box to complete the sentences.

read	wrestling	sports
boxing	warriors	write

The Greeks had a very modern way of life. They were taught ______________ such as athletics, ______________ and ______________. Rich Greeks were trained to be ______________ but also learned how to ______________ and ______________, as well as being taught many other subjects.

- Write about any other aspects of Ancient Greek life that have influenced our lives today.

____

____

____

____

I know about the way of life of the Ancient Greeks. ☐

Name ______________________ Date ______________

How do we use Ancient Greek ideas today?

- The table below gives a list of subjects that an Ancient Greek pupil would have been taught. Under the heading 'Your subjects', list all the subjects you take at school.

Greek subjects	Your subjects
Reading Writing Mathematics Philosophy Fighting with weapons Athletics Sports – boxing, wrestling	

- We can see that the Greeks influenced what we do at school today. Choose an aspect of Ancient Greek life that you have studied and explain how it is different from life today.

____

____

____

____

____

I know that the Ancient Greeks have influenced school life today. ☐

Name ______________________ Date ______________

How do we use Ancient Greek ideas today?

- List four things we do today that were ideas from Ancient Greece.

1. ______________________

2. ______________________

3. ______________________

4. ______________________

- Why do we continue to do these things?

____

____

- How is modern-day drama linked to Ancient Greek drama?

____

____

____

- How is modern-day politics linked to Ancient Greek politics?

____

____

____

- How is modern-day architecture similar to architecture in Ancient Greece?

____

____

____

Record of Achievement

I know ways the Ancient Greeks influenced life today.
I can give reasons why the way of life in Ancient Greece and life today are similar in some ways. ☐

Name ______________________ Date ______________

How do we use Ancient Greek ideas today?

- Which modern-day Olympic events would the Ancient Greeks recognise?

____

____

____

- What modern-day Olympic events are exactly the same as the ones in Ancient Greece?

____

____

- What modern-day Olympic events are a little bit similar to the one in Ancient Greece?

____

____

- What modern-day Olympic events are completely different to the ones in Ancient Greece?

____

____

I can compare and contrast the ancient and modern versions of the Olympic games. ☐

Geography

Geography provides the children with an opportunity to use geographical vocabulary to describe the environment and different localities. They are encouraged to consider human and physical features and environmental issues.

In Year 6, the children can study 'Investigating rivers' (finding out about rivers and the effects they have on the landscape; 'The mountain environment' (investigating weather conditions and mountain environments across the globe) and 'Investigating coasts' (looking at coastal environments and the effects waves and people can have on the landscape).

Investigating rivers

Unit 14

✔ **Learning outcome** (page 60)
To identify how people affect the environment.

✔✔ **Learning outcome** (page 61)
To recognise ways in which people might try to manage the environment.

✔✔ **Learning outcome** (page 62)
To recognise physical processes relating to rivers and begin to appreciate how these can change the character of places.

✔✔✔ **Learning outcome** (page 63)
To give explanations for river features observed and relate local river work to generalisations about rivers elsewhere.

In this unit, children learn, through field work and research, about rivers and the effects they have on the landscape. The unit focuses on the components of the water cycle, how rivers erode, transport and deposit materials to produce particular landscape features, and the characteristics of a river system in another part of the world.

When working on this unit, make sure the children have become familiar with words and phrases relating to rivers (*water cycle, rainfall, source, spring, river, stream, hill, slope, steep, mountain, waterfall, valley, channel, lake, mouth, erosion, pollution, landscape, tributary, reservoir, drain, weir, floodplain, meander, gorge, rapids, estuary, delta, weathering, transportation, deposition*).

Photocopiable page 60 requires the children to look at an illustration and describe ways in which water from rivers is used and how people have affected the water. For photocopiable page 61, children are asked to describe problems caused by flooding and how rivers can be managed to stop flooding. Children completing photocopiable page 62 are asked to look at an illustration of a river in the past and another illustration of the same river in the present and describe how (and why) the river has changed shape at two different points. For photocopiable page 63, children have to name a river they have studied and label some river features on an illustration. They are then required to describe a journey along the river in the illustration, using information about land and river features.

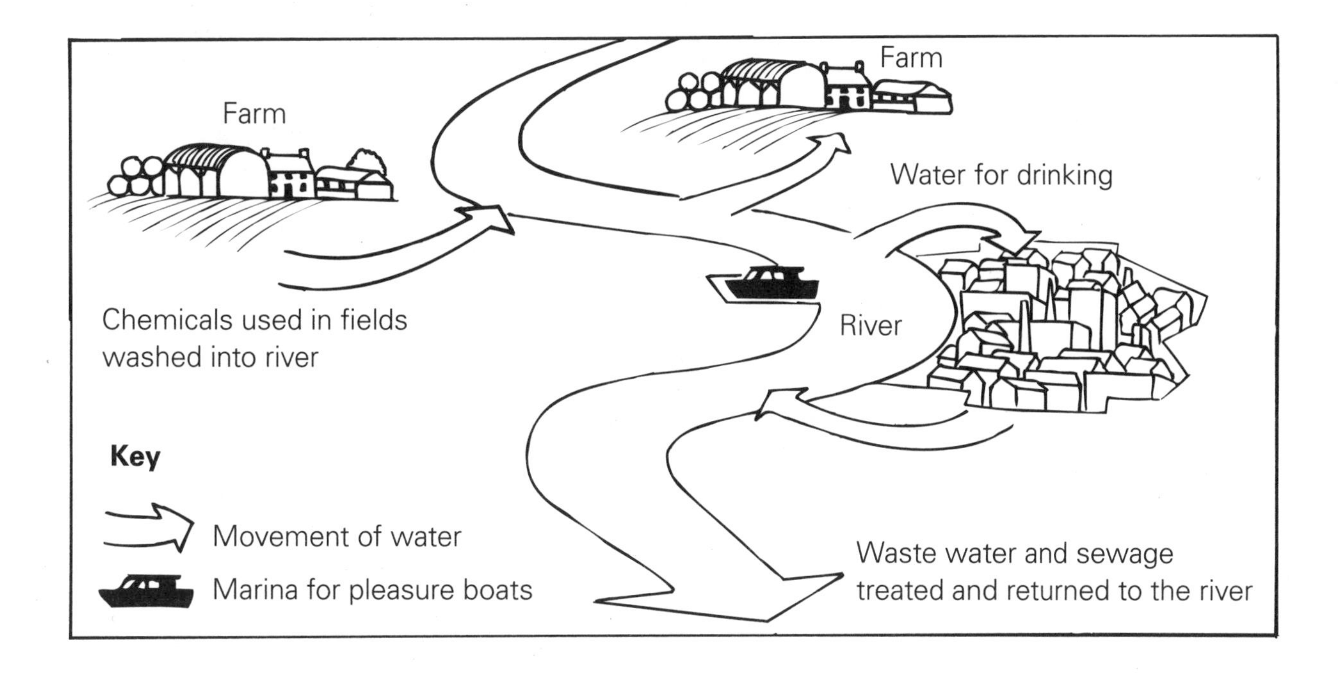

The mountain environment

Unit 15

✔ **Learning outcome** (page 64)
To relate questions to a mountain environment studied.

✔✔ **Learning outcome** (page 65)
To describe varying weather conditions in the world.

✔✔✔ **Learning outcome** (page 66)
To understand how different weather conditions can influence the way in which an area is developed.

✔✔✔✔ **Learning outcome** (page 67)
To plot detailed weather information and show understanding of the links between cause and effect.

In this unit, the children are encouraged to investigate, through research, places in the UK and further afield that have a similar physical environment. The unit builds on earlier work (such as studying a contrasting locality) and children are expected to use a wide range of resources including pictures, CD-ROMs and the Internet.

When working on this unit, make sure the children have become familiar with words and phrases relating to a mountain area (*environment, mountain, landscape, weather data, season, blizzard, avalanche, snowstorm, snowdrift, tourism, litter, erosion*).

For photocopiable page 64 children are expected to correctly label a diagram of a mountain. They are also required to describe how the climate would differ at certain points on the mountain. Children completing photocopiable page 65 are asked to consider the Arctic, Sahara Desert and the United Kingdom. They have to describe the weather in all three places, referring to temperature and rainfall. For photocopiable page 66, children are asked to explain how different weather conditions affect peoples' lives. Photocopiable page 67 requires the children to look at some information on temperature and rainfall and then plot the information on a bar graph. They are also required to describe what happens to rainfall and temperature in the summer months.

Investigating coasts

Unit 23

✔ **Learning outcome** (page 68)
To understand that waves and human activity affect coastal environments.

✔✔ **Learning outcomes** (page 69)
To describe the main features of coastal environments and recognise the processes of erosion and deposition in coastal environments. To begin to understand how these processes shape and change the coastline.

✔✔✔ **Learning outcomes** (page 70)
To recognise and explain the processes and features evident within a range of coastal environments. To recognise how places and environments may be managed sustainably.

In this unit, the children will study coastal environments and the effects waves and humans have on them.

When working on this unit, make sure the children have become familiar with words and phrases relating to coasts (*coast, erosion, transportation, deposition, waves, tide, rock, headland, cliff, cave, arch, stack, bay, beach, shingle, sand, groynes, sea walls*). They may also use *slope failure, cliff retreat, spit, longshore drift, erosion landforms, depositional landforms.*

Photocopiable page 68 requires the children to look at a diagram of a beach and illustrate where the sand will be in the future. They are then required to look at two other diagrams and describe how the sea is affecting the cliffs and how the building of groynes has altered the beach. Children completing photocopiable page 69 are expected to draw the shape of a coast after the sea has worn away the rocks and to consider why the hardness of the rock makes the coastline shape uneven. They are also required to label erosion and deposition on a map. For photocopiable page 70, the children are asked to look at a map and label coastal features using words from a list. They are then required to describe how the sea makes caves, arches and stacks and what causes beaches and spits to be made. They are also asked to suggest ways to manage the environment.

Name ______________________ Date ______________

Investigating rivers

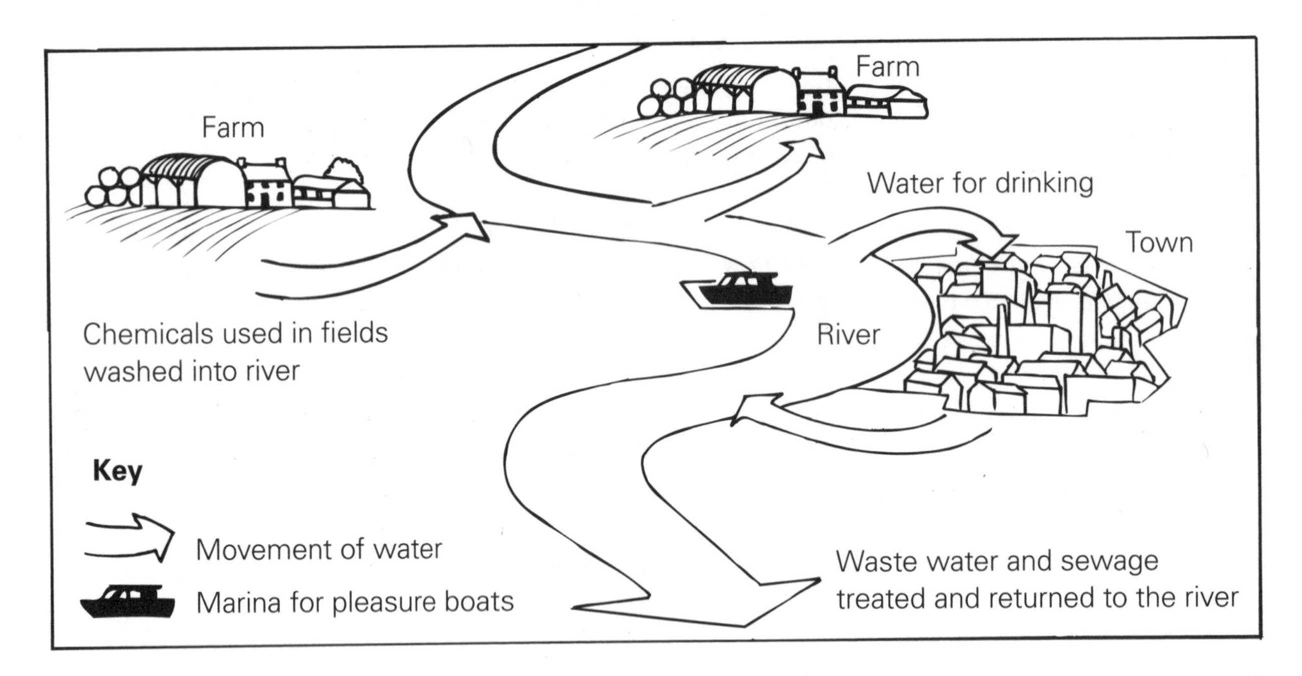

- Write down three ways that people use the water in the river.

1. ______________________
2. ______________________
3. ______________________

- Write down two ways that people have affected the water.

1. ______________________
2. ______________________

- Write down how tourism might affect a river in a bad way.

____

____

- Write down how tourism might affect a good way.

____

____

I can identify how people affect the environment. ☐

Name ______________________ Date ______________

Investigating rivers

Too much rain or lots of melting snow can cause rivers to flood. Flooding can cause all sorts of problems.

- Write down **three** problems caused by flooding.

1. ______________________

____

____

2. ______________________

____

____

3. ______________________

____

- Write down **three** ways that rivers can be managed to stop them from flooding.

1. ______________________

____

2. ______________________

____

3. ______________________

____

I can recognise ways in which people try to manage the environment. ☐

Name ______________________ Date ______________

Investigating rivers

Below is a map showing part of a river in the past. Next to it is another map showing the same river as it looks today.

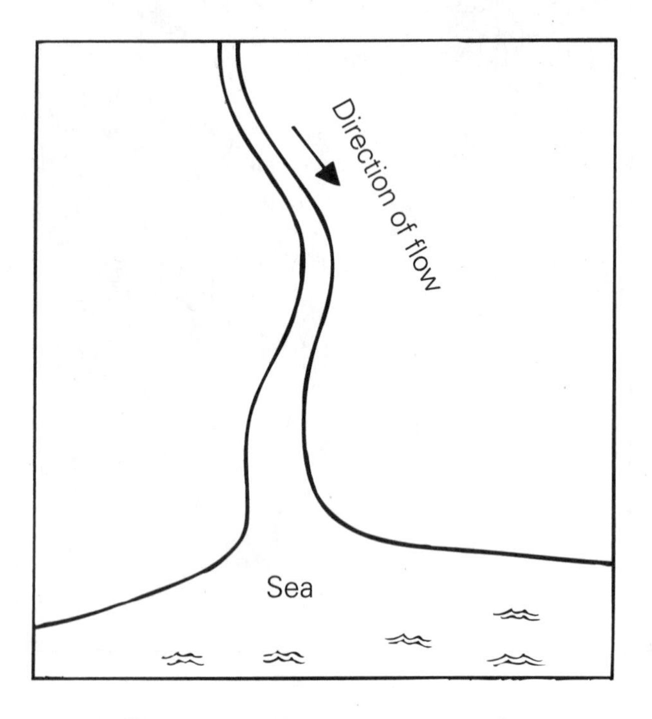

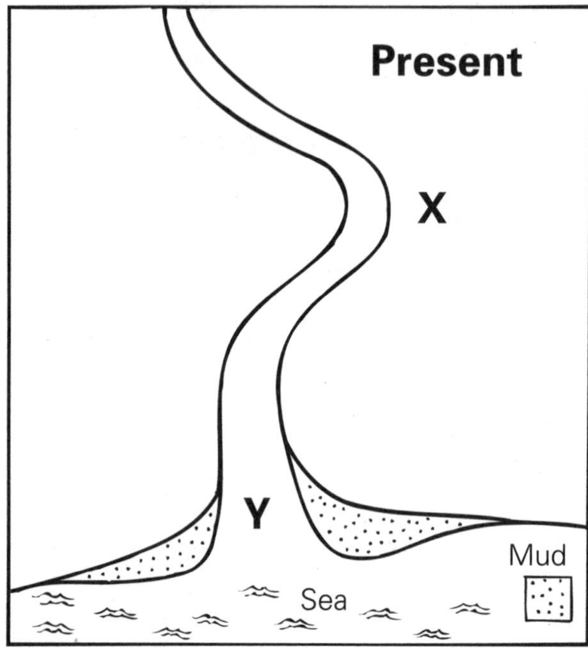

- How has the river changed its shape at point **X**?

____

____

- What has caused this?

____

____

- What has the river caused to happen at point **Y**?

____

____

I can recognise physical processes relating to rivers and begin to appreciate how these can change the character of places. ☐

Name ______________________________ Date ____________________

Investigating rivers

- Write the name of a river you have studied. ____________________

- On the map below, label the river features shown.

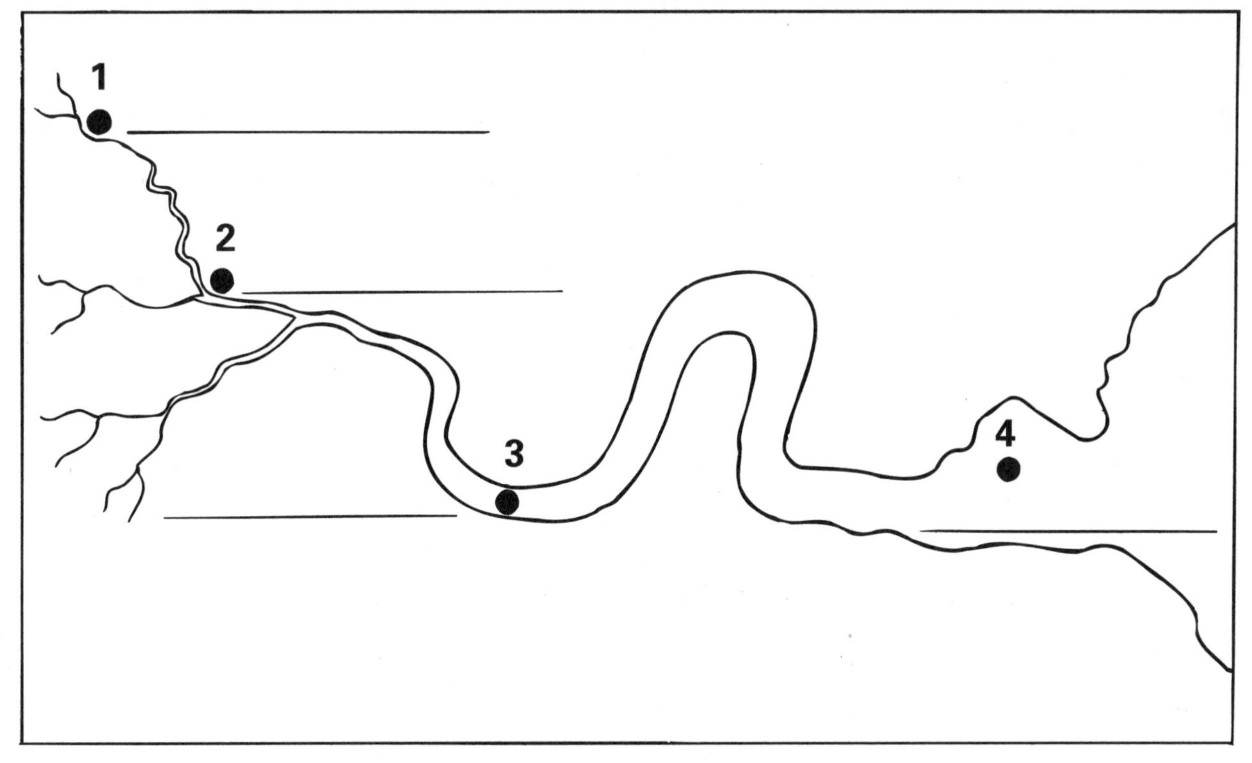

- Describe a journey along the river shown in the map, from point 1 to point 4. Include information about the land and river features.

____

____

____

____

____

____

I can offer explanations for river features observed and relate local river work to generalisations about rivers elsewhere. ☐

Name ______________________ Date ______________

The mountain environment

- Look at the diagram of a mountain below and add these labels at the correct places.

valley **bottom** **summit** **steep slope** **slope**

- Mountains have different climates to lowland areas. Describe how the climate on the mountain at point **X** will be different to point **Y**.

____

____

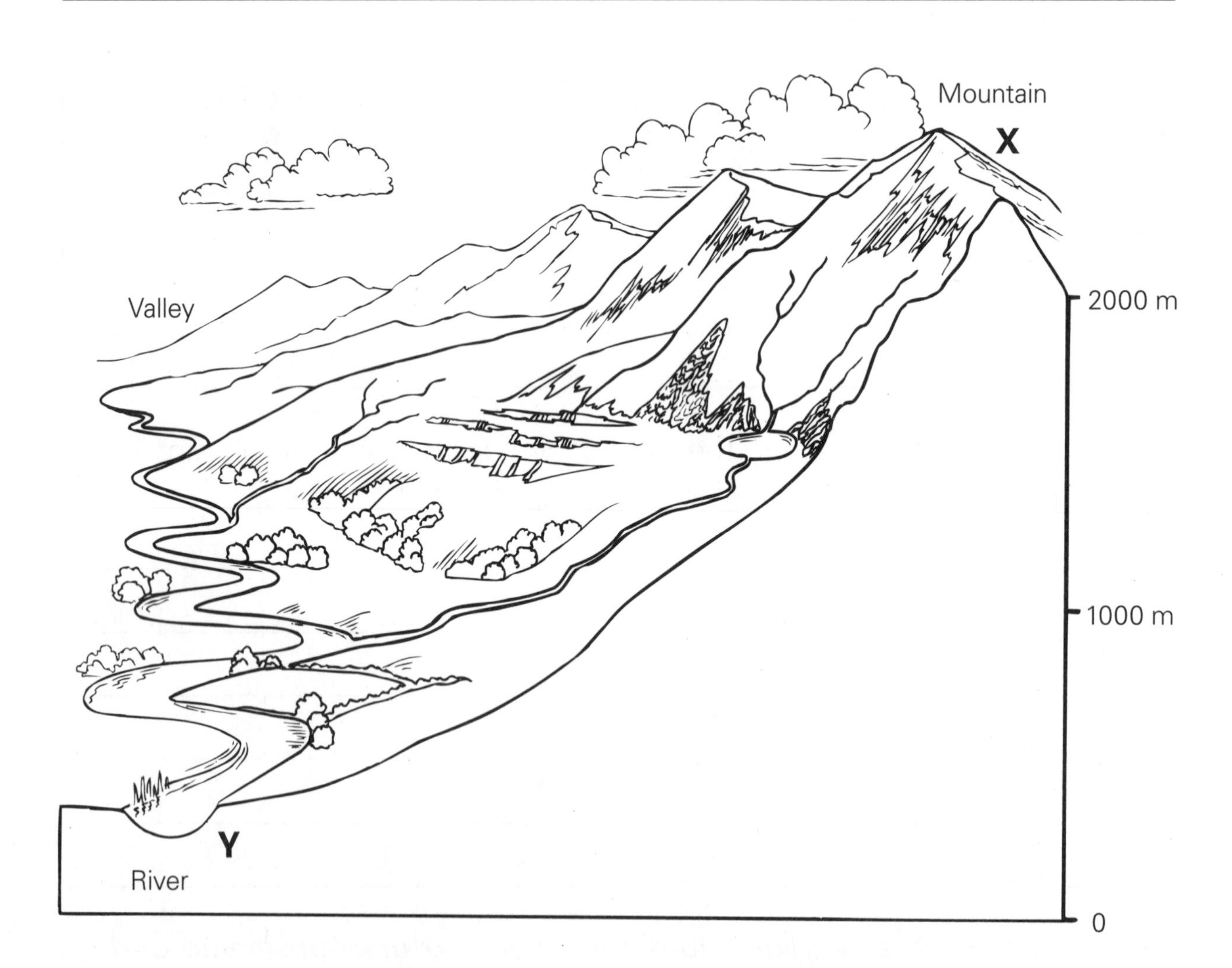

Record of Achievement

I can relate questions to a mountain environment I have studied. ☐

Name ______________________ Date ______________

The mountain environment

- Describe the different weather conditions in the places below. Remember to refer to temperature and rainfall.

Arctic

____
____
____
____
____
____

Sahara Desert

____
____
____
____
____
____

United Kingdom

____
____
____
____
____
____

I can describe varying weather conditions in the world. ☐

Name ______________________ Date ______________

The mountain environment

- The weather affects how places develop. Some places are very cold, like the arctic and antarctic. What would it be like to live in the arctic?

____

____

- What sort of work could people living in the arctic do?

____

- Some places are very hot, like the Sahara Desert. What would it be like to live in the Sahara Desert?

____

____

- What sort of work could people living in the Sahara Desert do?

____

- Some places are very wet, like the rainforest. What would it be like to live in a rainforest?

____

____

- What sort of work could people living in a rainforest do?

____

I understand how different weather conditions can influence the way in which an area is developed. ☐

Name ______________________________ Date ________________

The mountain environment

- Which place has a climate that is not too hot or cold?

Place A

Months	J	F	M	A	M	J	J	A	S	O	N	D
Temperature	10	11	12	14	16	18	20	18	16	14	12	11
Rainfall	30	35	30	25	25	20	15	20	25	30	35	40

Place B

Months	J	F	M	A	M	J	J	A	S	O	N	D
Temperature	30	31	31	31	31	31	30	30	30	30	30	30
Rainfall	95	100	105	95	90	95	95	95	90	95	100	100

Place C

Months	J	F	M	A	M	J	J	A	S	O	N	D
Temperature	-20	-15	-15	-10	-5	0	0	5	0	-5	-10	-15
Rainfall	10	15	20	15	15	20	15	15	15	10	10	10

- For the place you have chosen, draw a bar graph below to show its rainfall, then a line graph to show its temperature.

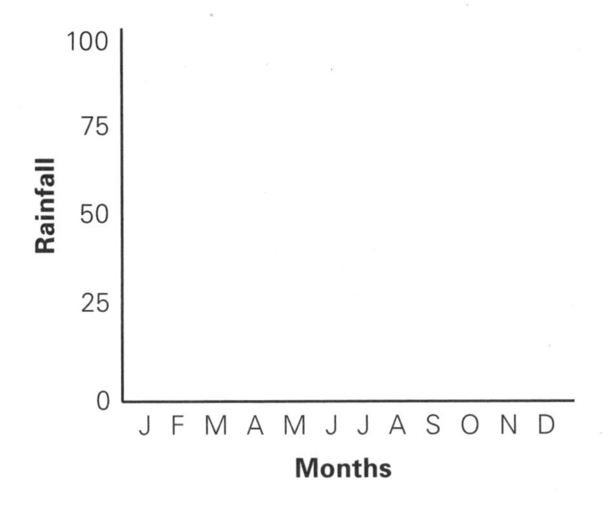

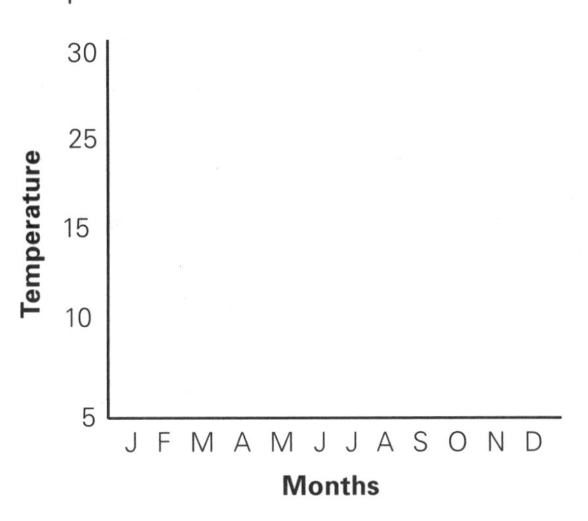

- What do you notice happens to the temperature and the rainfall in the summer months?

____

____

Record of Achievement

I can find a range of source materials and plot detailed weather information. I can show understanding of the links between cause and effect. ☐

Name ______________________ Date ______________

Investigating coasts

- On the map below, put a cross on the beach to show where the sand grains will be in the future.

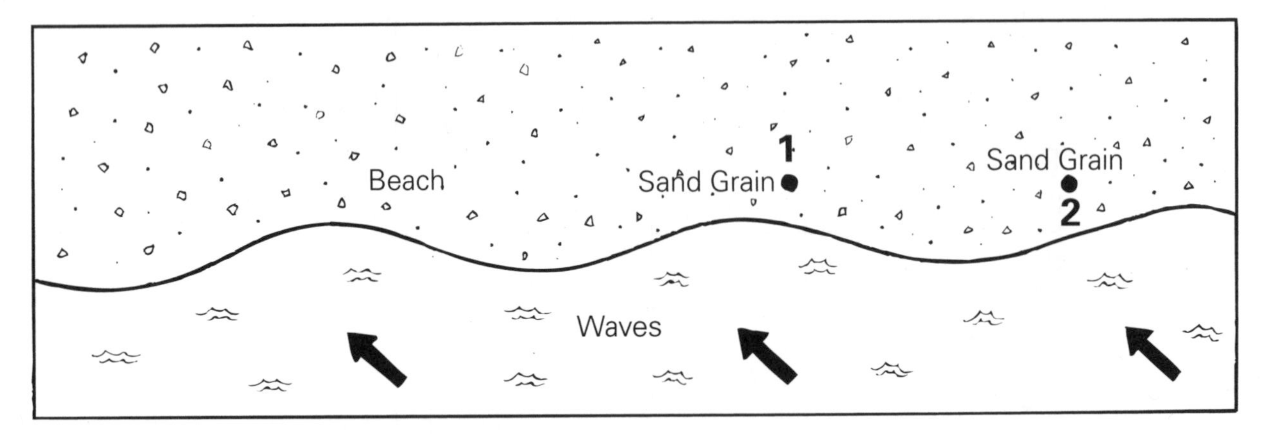

- Look at the diagrams below.

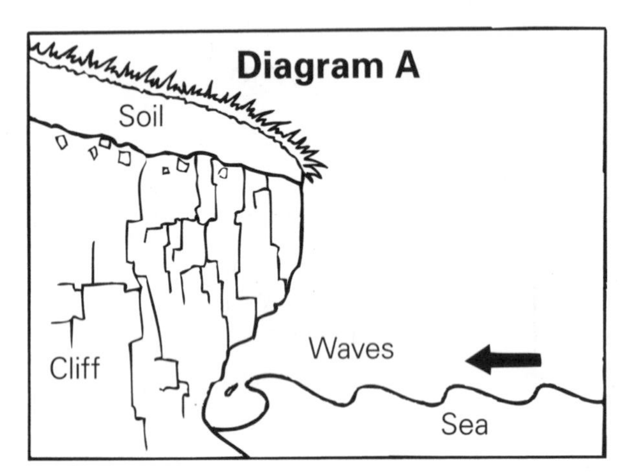

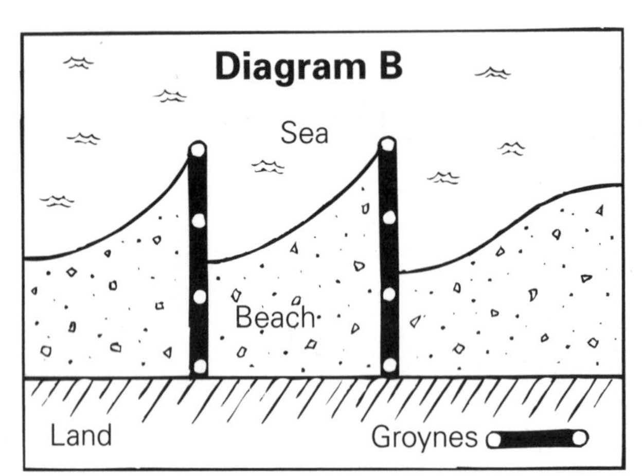

In **Diagram A** what is the sea doing to the cliffs?

____

____

In **Diagram B** how has the building of groynes altered the beach?

____

____

I can understand that waves and human activity affect coastal environments. ☐

Name ______________________ Date ______________

Investigating coasts

- **Box A** contains an illustration showing the rock formation in a particular place. After many years, the rocks have been worn away by the sea. In **Box B**, draw the new shape of the coast.

Box A

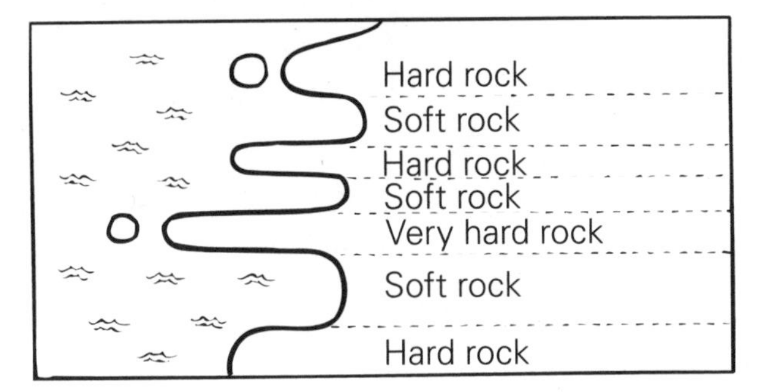

Box B

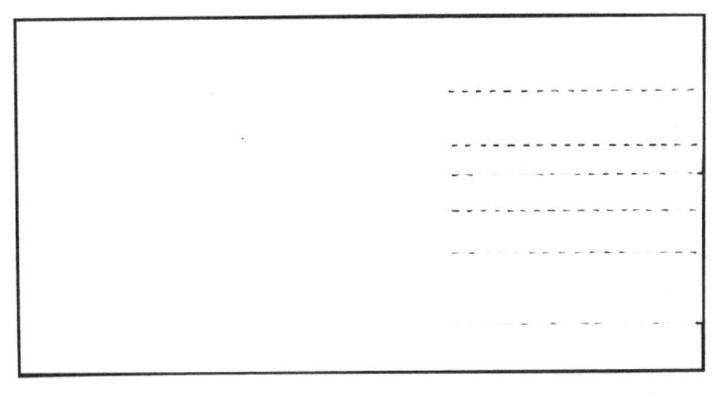

- Why does the hardness of the rock make the coastline shape uneven?

____

____

- Describe what happens to the particles of rock that have been worn away by the sea.

____

____

- Label 'erosion' and 'deposition' on this map.

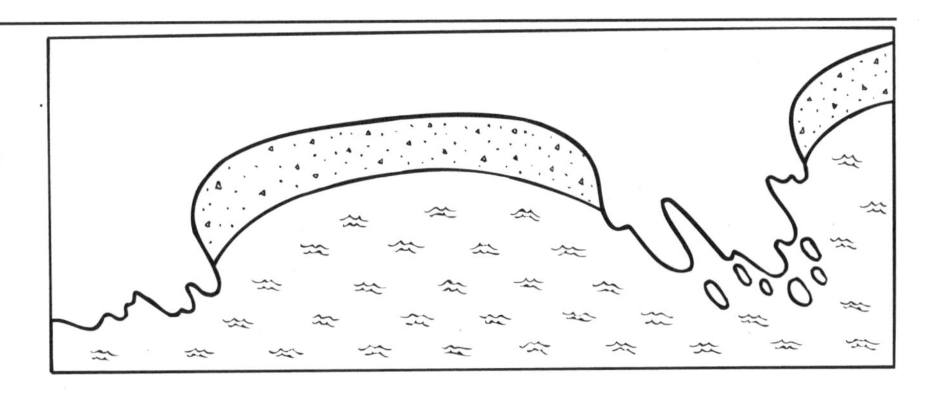

Record of Achievement

I can describe the main features of coastal environments. I recognise the processes of erosion and deposition in coastal environments and am beginning to understand how these processes shape and change the coastline ☐

Name ______________________________ Date ____________________

Investigating coasts

- Look at the diagram below. Using the words from the list, label all the coastal features you can see.

spit cliffs beach stack arch cave headlands

- How does the sea make caves, arches and stacks?

____

____

- What causes beaches and spits to be made?

____

____

- People enjoy going to the coast for their holidays. What would be needed at these places to ensure that they do not suffer from pollution and damage by large numbers of visitors?

____

____

I can recognise and explain the processes and features evident within a range of coastal environments. I recognise how places and environments may be managed sustainably. ☐

ICT

Information Communications Technology (ICT) provides children with the opportunity to build ICT capabilities and develop their skills at using hardware and software to manipulate information in problem solving, recording and expressive work.

In Year 6, the children will gain experience in the use of multimedia authoring packages, spreadsheets, input devices attached to a computer and the Internet. It is assumed that most of the work is done on the computer and the photocopiable sheets are seen only as a record of children having acquired and developed the skills associated with ICT.

Multimedia presentation

Unit 6A

✔ **Learning outcome** (page 76)
To create a multimedia page.

✔✔ **Learning outcome** (page 77)
To assemble a set of linked multimedia pages.

✔✔✔ **Learning outcome** (page 78)
To assemble a set of linked multimedia pages, which offer the user a variety of options.

In this unit, the children learn to create a multimedia presentation using text, images and sound.

When working on this unit make sure that the children have become familiar with words and phrases related to technical vocabulary (*interactive, hot spot/hyperlink, attach, hypertext*).

The photocopiables in this unit require the children to have had access to a multimedia authoring package. They will have learned how to create links between pages and show sensitivity to the needs of the audience. It is assumed the majority of the children's work for this unit will have been done on the computer when they will have had the opportunity to organise, refine, and present a set of linked multimedia pages which incorporate images, sounds and text. Photocopiable page 76 asks the children to stick a printout of their multimedia page in the space provided, as a record of the work undertaken. Children completing photocopiable page 77 should be able to draw a diagram to show the links between the multimedia pages created for their presentation. Photocopiable page 78 asks the children to identify the subject they chose for their presentation, and their intended audience. They then have to stick on a printout or draw a diagram of a page of their presentation that they think offers the user a variety of options.

Spreadsheet modelling

Unit 6B

✔ **Learning outcome** (page 79)
To use a spreadsheet to calculate totals.

✔✔ **Learning outcome** (page 80)
To explore the effects of changing data in a spreadsheet.

✔✔✔ **Learning outcome** (page 81)
To enter data into a spreadsheet, change data, make predictions and use the spreadsheet to test them.

In this unit the children learn how to use a spreadsheet to explore a mathematical model.

When working on this unit, ensure that the children have become familiar with words and phrases related to technical vocabulary (*spreadsheet, cell, formula, calculate, data, model*).

The photocopiable pages in this unit require the children to have had access to spreadsheet software and have been taught to use the necessary formulae. They will have explored how changes in a spreadsheet affect results and will know how to identify simple rules. It is assumed that children will apply what they have learned in this unit when exploring mathematical and scientific models. Photocopiable page 79 asks the children to enter some data into a spreadsheet and use formulae to calculate totals based on the data. Children completing photocopiable page 80 should be able to enter data into a spreadsheet, use formulae to make calculations, and explain the effects of altering certain data on the spreadsheet. Photocopiable page 81 asks the children to enter data into a spreadsheet, use formulae to calculate the total and average scores for each child, make predictions and explain the effects of altering data.

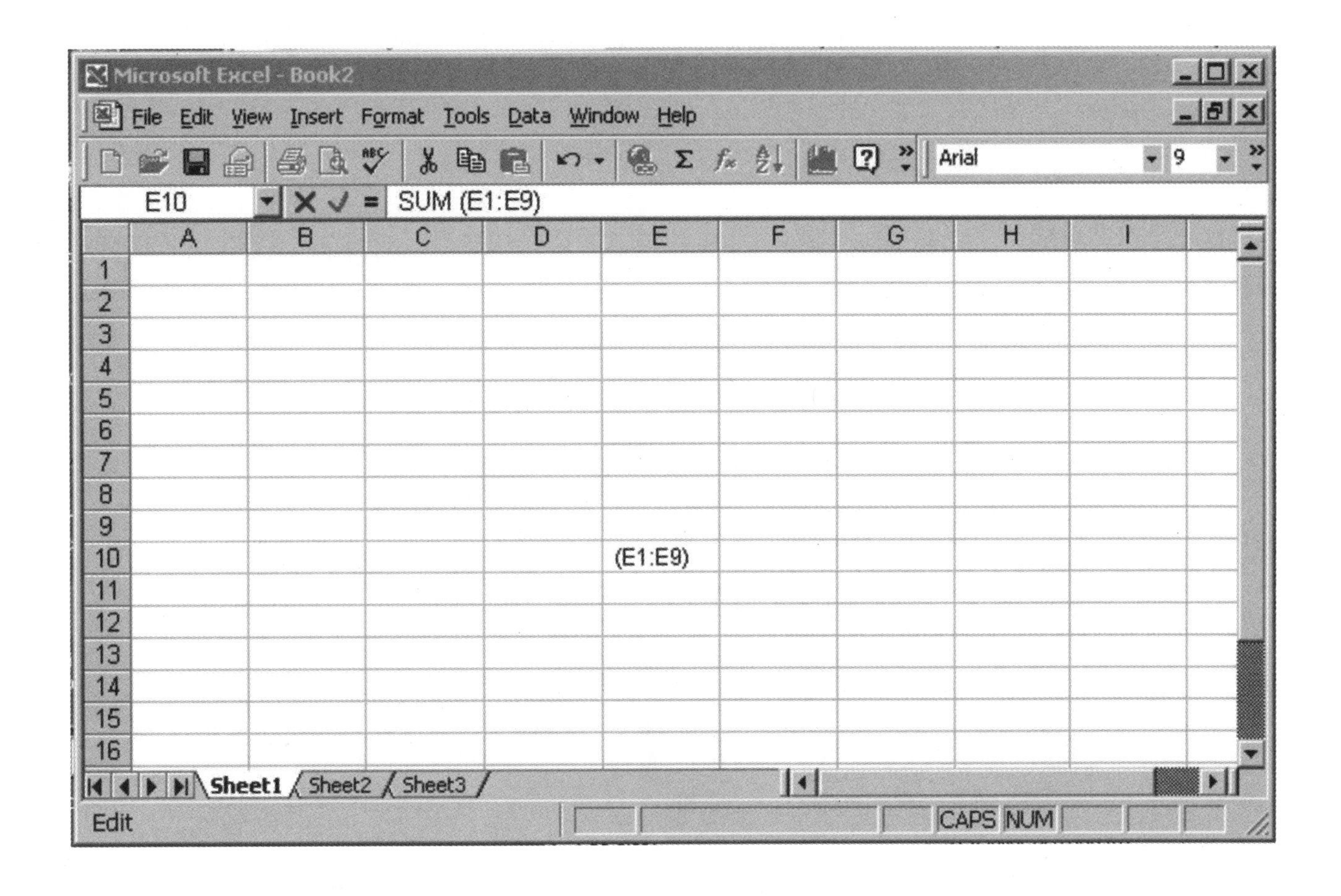

Control and monitoring – what happens when?

Unit 6C

✓ Learning outcome (page 82)
To write a procedure, with help, to turn a light bulb on and off.

✓✓ Learning outcome (page 83)
To write simple procedures to turn on lights and sound alarms.

✓✓✓ Learning outcome (page 84)
To string procedures together, recognising patterns in programming

In following this unit, the children will have learned how to use input devices or switches to control a process.

When working on this unit make sure that the children have become familiar with words and phrases related to technical vocabulary (*if, then, until*).

The photocopiable pages in this unit require the children to have learned that it is possible to attach devices – such as pressure pads, light sensors, magnetic switches, on/off switches or other devices – to a control box. They will have learned that the computer can then be programmed to carry out a process when it detects some sort of change. They will also have had the opportunity to learn the new control language necessary to program to make such decisions. Photocopiable page 82 asks the children to identify two systems that use monitoring to control events. They are also asked to write a procedure to make a light bulb flash on a model lighthouse. Children completing photocopiable page 83 should be able to draw an annotated diagram of a model they have made that incorporates lights that go on and off and alarms that sound when the door or window is opened. They are also required to write procedures for two named events associated with their model. Photocopiable page 84 asks the children to describe how automatic doors work and name three output devices that could be used to control automatic doors. They are also required to write two procedures to open and close the doors.

Using the Internet to search large databases and interpret information

Unit 6D

✔ **Learning outcome** (page 85)
To search the Internet to find appropriate information.

✔✔ **Learning outcome** (page 86)
To form questions to initiate an Internet search for specific information.

✔✔✔ **Learning outcome** (page 87)
To search the Internet for specific information using a range of operators.

In this unit, children will learn how to use large sources of information, such as those found on the Internet

When working on this unit, ensure that the children have become familiar with words and phrases related to technical vocabulary (*audience, Internet, index, bookmark, URL, search engine, bias, string, hyperlink*).

The photocopiable pages in this unit require the children to have learned how to use, skim read and take in information, and to be able to own it for themselves and interpret it with others. They will have learned how to be critical of content and may be able to check for different viewpoints. They will also have learned how to present researched information in a form suitable for the needs of the audience. Photocopiable page 85 asks the children to search the Internet for appropriate information, identify the website address they found most useful in their work and stick on a printout that records their skills in copying and pasting text and pictures from the Internet into a word document. Children completing photocopiable page 86 should be able to search the Internet for information using key words of their choice and refining the search when they feel it is necessary. Photocopiable page 87 asks the children to make a record of the search engines they used to find the information they were looking for and to list three pieces of information they learned from their searches.

Name ______________________________ Date ____________________

Multimedia presentation

- In the space provided, stick an example of a multimedia page you have assembled using a multimedia authoring package.

- Describe how you assembled the page and who it was intended for.

____

____

____

____

I can use a multimedia authoring package to assemble images, sound and text on a multimedia page. ☐

Name ______________________ Date ______________

Multimedia presentation

- Draw a diagram of the multimedia pages you assembled and show how your pages are linked.

I can use a multimedia authoring package to create a set of linked multimedia pages which include images, sound and text. ☐

Name ______________________ Date ______________

Multimedia presentation

- Identify the subject you chose for your multimedia presentation.

____

- Describe the audience for which it was intended.

____

____

- In the space provided, draw a diagram or stick a printout of a page from your presentation that offers the user a variety of options. Label these options.

Record of Achievement

I can use a multimedia package to present a set of linked multimedia pages, which offer the user a variety of options and present information that matches the needs of the audience. ☐

Name ______________________ Date ______________

Spreadsheet modelling

Recorded below are the number of goals scored for eight football teams in an Under 11s Sunday League over a period of five weeks.

Team	Week 1	Week 2	Week 3	Week 4	Week 5
Wingchester	2	1	0	0	4
Beckfield	1	1	3	0	0
Scampton	0	2	0	3	1
Preston	2	1	2	4	3
Rawsthorne	1	1	0	1	0
Cleanington	3	1	0	2	0
Hampton	0	1	1	0	2
Sporcastle	2	1	0	4	0

- Enter the data into a spreadsheet on your computer.
- Calculate the total number of goals scored in Week 4 on your spreadsheet. ______________________
- Write the formula you used to calculate the total.

____

Record of Achievement *I can use a spreadsheet to calculate totals.* ☐

Name ____________________ Date ____________

Spreadsheet modelling

Recorded below are the rugby scores for a season in a league.

Games	1	2	3	4	5	6	7	8	9	10
Teams										
Tiber	27	11	5	13	24	9	21	22	14	14
Rhone	13	6	18	14	37	29	25	17	16	18
Rhine	56	33	19	39	49	32	25	23	17	41
Nile	44	25	20	41	13	23	33	26	25	26
Ouse	10	12	19	14	20	19	24	23	19	16
Trent	19	13	17	15	9	11	17	14	16	10
Tees	63	40	35	27	54	39	31	39	44	26
Tyne	32	19	17	20	36	37	21	42	33	25
Tweed	47	21	11	13	33	29	39	18	24	22
Calder	15	21	16	17	35	11	19	25	25	28

- Enter the information into a spreadsheet and calculate the season total for each team, using a formula of your choice.

The formula I used for calculating the season total for team was:

____

- Unfortunately, it was found that there had been a mistake in recording the number of points for the Tees team and in game 5 the score should have read '45' instead of '54'. In game 10, it should have read '66' instead of '26'. Enter the new data into your spreadsheet and explain the effect it had on the seasonal totals.

____

____

- Would this change in data affect the weekly total for the number of points scored in the league? Explain your answer.

____

____

____

I can explore the effects of changing data in a spreadsheet. ☐

Name ______________________ Date ______________

Spreadsheet modelling

- Copy into a spreadsheet these weekly test scores for a group of children.

	Week 1	Week 2	Week 3	Week 4	Week 5	Week 6	Week 7	Week 8	Total	Average
Tom	27	11	5	13	24	9	21	22		
Rhona	13	6	18	14	37	29	25	17		
Danny	56	33	19	39	49	32	25	23		
Nina	44	25	20	41	13	23	33	26		
Olivia	10	12	19	14	20	19	24	23		
Tyler	19	13	17	15	9	11	17	14		
Toby	63	40	35	27	54	39	31	39		
Jane	32	19	17	20	36	37	21	42		
Paul	47	21	11	13	33	29	39	18		
David	15	21	16	17	35	11	19	25		

- Calculate the total score for each child and their average score.

- Record the formulae you used for Olivia.

The total score formula for Olivia was: ______________

The average score formula for Olivia was: ______________

- What effect would changing the spelling of Olivia's name have on the above results?

____

- What effect does it have on the spreadsheet if you change the scores for Danny by increasing them all by 10?

____

- Predict one other effect of changing the data.

____

____

Record of Achievement

I can explore the effects of changing data in a spreadsheet, make predictions and use a spreadsheet to test them. ☐

Name ______________________ Date ______________

Control and monitoring – what happens when?

- Identify two systems that use monitoring to control events.

- Describe how one of the systems might work.

____

____

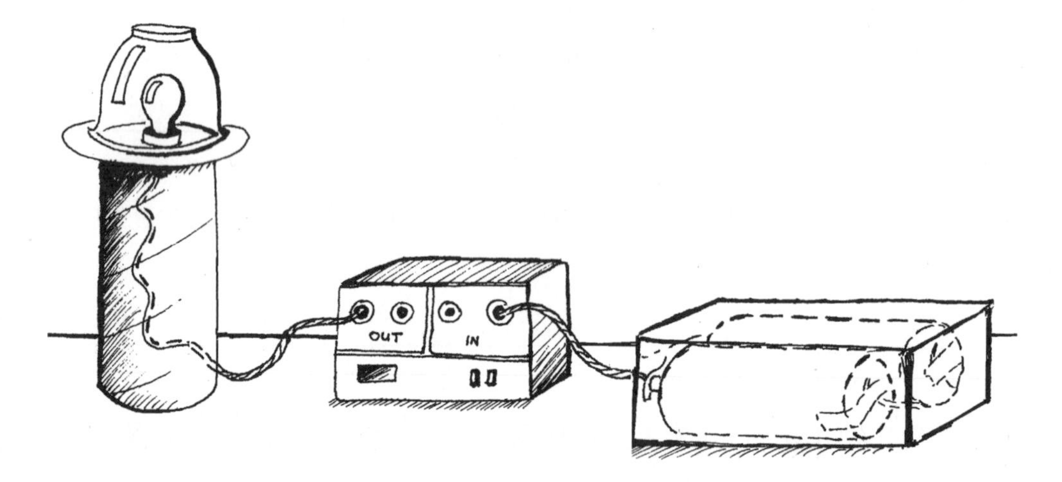

- Write a procedure to make the light bulb flash every second.

____

____

____

____

I can, with help, write a procedure to turn a light bulb on and off. ☐

Name ______________________________ Date ____________________

Control and monitoring – what happens when?

- Draw an annotated diagram of the model you made.

- Record below the sequence of instructions you used for the following events.

To switch lights on at night and off in the morning.	For the alarm to sound if the door or window is opened.

Record of Achievement

I can write simple procedures to turn on lights and sound alarms. ☐

Name ______________________ Date ______________

Control and monitoring – what happens when?

- Describe how you think the automatic doors in the picture operate.

____

____

- Name **three** output devices that could be used to control the doors.

______________ ______________ ______________

- Describe the system you would use to control the doors.

____

____

- Write **two** procedures to open and close the doors.

1. ____

____

2. ____

____

Record of Achievement *I can string procedures together, recognising patterns in programming.* ☐

Name ____________________ Date ____________

Using the Internet to search large databases and to interpret information

- What information did your teacher ask you to search for?

____

____

____

- Identify the web address of a site you found useful in your search

- In the space below, stick a printout as an example of work in which you copied text and pictures from an Internet site for others to view.

I can search the internet to find appropriate information and copy text and pictures for others to view. ☐

Name ______________________ Date ______________

Using the Internet to search large databases and to interpret information

- What information did your teacher ask you to search for?

____

____

- How did you word your search? (If you then refined your search further, record that search also.)

____

____

- In the space below, stick an example of work that shows you can copy text and pictures from an Internet site and paste them into a word document.

I can search the Internet forming my own questions to find specific information and then present this information to an audience. ☐

Name ______________________ Date ______________

Using the Internet to search large databases and to interpret information

- Identify the information you searched the Internet for.

____

____

- List the search engines you used.

- Record how you continually refined your search ideas.

- Identify three pieces of information you found as a result of your searches.

1. ____

2. ____

3. ____

Record of Achievement *I can search the internet using a variety of operators to find specific information.* ☐

Art and design

Art and design provides children with the opportunity to improve their control of materials, tools and techniques and become more confident in using visual and tactile elements. It also gives them the opportunity to increase their critical awareness of the roles and purposes of art in different times and cultures by commenting on works of art and asking questions like: 'What is this work about?' and 'Why was it made?'.

In Year 6, the children will have the opportunity to learn how to convey movement in their work, use textiles to create headwear and costumes from different times and cultures, and explore rural and/or urban landscape as a starting point for two-dimensional work.

People in action

Unit 6A

✔ **Learning outcome** (page 93)
To evaluate a sketch that communicates ideas of movement.

✔✔ **Learning outcome** (page 94)
To represent figures and forms and comment on ideas, methods and approaches used in their own work.

✔✔✔ **Learning outcome** (page 95)
To manipulate materials and techniques, using visual and tactile qualities to communicate ideas about movement, and select relevant information to use in their work.

In following this unit, the children will have learnt how to convey movement in their work. This unit builds on Unit 3A 'Portraying relationships', where the children used compositional skills to portray the relationship between figures and Unit 4A 'Viewpoints' where the children made a sequence of images.

When working on this unit, make sure that the children are familiar with words and phrases related to the ways in which movement is shown in visual form (*film, animated cartoons, cartoon sequences);* movement (*action, repetition, sequence, drift, dynamic, flowing, motion, rhythm)*; human form *(pose, position, gesture, open/closed shape)*; tone *(lightness, shade, contrast)*; colour *(brilliant, glowing, dark, faded, expressive)* and representation *(depict, portray, figurative, abstract).*

The photocopiable pages in this unit require the children to have explored dynamic activities such as sport, dance, drama and music as a starting point for their work. They will have looked at how the idea of movement is shown in different kinds of art and have experimented with different methods and techniques to show movement. Photocopiable page 93 asks the children to sketch a figure that communicates visual ideas of movement and then asks the children to evaluate the sketch by commenting on the methods and techniques they used. Children completing photocopiable page 94 should be able to draw two different sketches that show the idea of movement and then make a comparative analysis of the sketches. Photocopiable page 95 asks the children to draw a picture that communicates movement and describe how they manipulated materials and techniques, using visual and tactile qualities taken from another piece of work.

What a performance

Unit 6B

✔ **Learning outcome** (page 96)
To explore ideas about headwear and record information they have collected in their research.

✔✔ **Learning outcome** (page 97)
To communicate ideas and meanings in a piece of headwear they have made and evaluate their work.

✔✔✔ **Learning outcome** (page 98)
To select and use information to develop their work and evaluate their finished work in a meaningful way.

In this unit, the children will have investigated headwear and costume worn in different times and cultures, including theatre costume. This unit builds on Unit 4B 'Take a seat' and Unit 5B 'Talking textiles', where children gained skills and experience of using textiles and construction materials to create three-dimensional form.

When working on this unit, make sure the children are familiar with words and phrases related to headwear and costumes designed for different purposes (*for the theatre, carnival, celebration*); making skills (*knot, tie, fringe, fold*); textile techniques (*applique, quilting*) and forces (*weight, balance, movement*).

The photocopiable pages in this unit require the children to have designed and made a piece of headwear for a character in a story using a range of textiles and other materials. They will have explored ideas about headwear, collected materials and information for their work, matched visual and tactile elements to their intentions and learnt how to comment on ideas, methods and approaches they saw in others' work and adapt and improve their own work. Photocopiable page 96 asks the children to record some of the information/ideas they collected in their research about headwear. Children completing photocopiable page 97 should have already completed their piece of headwear and drawn a picture or stuck a photo on the photocopiable as a record of their work. They are then asked to answer key questions. Photocopiable page 98 asks the children to identify three pieces of headwear from their research, which they think helped them develop their own design idea.

A sense of place

Unit 6C

✔ **Learning outcome** (page 99)
To comment on others' work.

✔✔ **Learning outcome** (page 100)
To collect visual and other information by observing and recording features of the environment.

✔✔✔ **Learning outcome** (page 101)
To paint a picture of the environment and evaluate the finished work.

In following this unit the children will have explored the rural and/or urban landscape as a starting point for their two-dimensional work. This unit builds on Unit 5A 'Objects and meanings', where the children developed their painting skills and their knowledge of composition in a painting.

When working on this unit, make sure that the children are familiar with words and phrases related to landscape (*viewpoint, perspective, foreground, background*) architecture (*scale, enlarge*); visual elements (*relative size, colour, texture, pattern, detail, form*) and materials and processes (*acrylic paint, slab, mould, slip, impressed and incised pattern and texture*).

The photocopiable pages in this unit require the children to have recorded their observations of the landscape through drawing and photography. They will have used shape, form, space, colour, texture and pattern to develop and communicate their ideas in a painting. They will also have considered the ideas, methods and approaches of artists who have responded to landscapes in different ways. Photocopiable page 99 asks the children to make a copy of a painting of the environment by a famous artist whose work they have looked at in class. They are then required to answer a number of questions about the work. Children completing photocopiable page 100 should have explored ideas about the environment during a visit to a park or place of interest. For photocopiable page 101, children are required to stick in the space provided, a photo or draw a picture of the painting of the environment they have created. They are then required to answer key questions.

Visiting a museum, gallery or site

Unit 9

✔ **Learning outcome** (page 102)
To describe a place they have visited and explain how the visit has contributed to the work they are doing in class.

✔✔ **Learning outcome** (page 103)
To comment on objects seen on a visit and on how the information collected helped in their work.

✔✔✔ **Learning outcome** (page 104)
To comment on how and why objects came to be in a museum and how the museum carries out its social, cultural and other functions.

In following this unit, structure is provided for a visit to a museum, gallery or site, or any visit outside school.

When working on this unit, make sure that the children are familiar with words and phrases related to the physical form of museums and galleries, the social function of museums and galleries and the use of museums and galleries.

The photocopiable pages in this unit require the children to have visited a museum, gallery or site, or have been on any visit outside school. The visit would be most effectively used at the start or in the middle of a unit of work, so that work back at school could be based on the information and experience acquired. All photocopiable pages in this unit have been kept general so as to make them suitable for visits to many different venues. Photocopiable page 102 asks the children to draw a picture of the outside of the building they visited, or perhaps one of the rooms inside. They are then asked to describe what they saw inside and how they felt this visit contributed to the work they were doing in art. Children completing photocopiable page 103 should be able to draw and comment on a selection of objects seen on their visit to a museum, gallery or other suitable venue. Photocopiable page 104 asks the children to draw some objects they saw in a museum and comment on how and why they came to be in a museum.

Name ______________________________ Date ____________________

People in action

- Sketch a figure that shows movement.

- Describe the method or techniques you used in your sketch to communicate your ideas of movement.

____

____

____

- Evaluate your work by suggesting ways of improving it.

____

____

____

Record of Achievement

I can communicate my ideas of movement and am able to evaluate my own work ☐

Name ______________________ Date ______________

People in action

- Make two sketches that communicate movement in different ways.

- Compare and comment on the two sketches. Remember to refer to your ideas, methods and approaches.

____

____

____

____

Record of Achievement

I can represent figures and forms in movement and comment on ideas, methods and approaches used in my work. ☐

Name ______________________ Date ______________

People in action

- Draw a picture that communicates ideas about movement.

- Describe any relevant information you used to help you communicate your ideas about movement.

____

____

____

- Describe how you manipulated materials and techniques, using visual and tactile qualities from another piece of your work to communicate your ideas about movement.

____

____

____

Record of Achievement

I can manipulate materials and techniques, using visual and tactile qualities to communicate ideas about movement, and select relevant information to use in my work. ☐

Name ______________________________ Date ____________________

What a performance

- In the boxes below, show some of the ideas and information you have collected or researched about headwear.

Record of Achievement *I can explore ideas about headwear and collect materials and information for my work.* ☐

Name ______________________ Date ______________

What a performance

- In the space below, stick a photograph or draw a picture of the piece of headwear you made when following this unit.

- Make comments about your work under the following headings.

What materials and techniques did you use?

____

____

How did these match your ideas?

____

____

What did others think of your work?

____

____

Record of Achievement

I can communicate ideas and meanings in a piece of headwear I have made and evaluate my work. ☐

Name ______________________________ Date ____________________

What a performance

- Draw three different examples of headwear from your research that you feel helped you develop your design ideas for your piece of headwear.

- Describe how you adapted and refined your work to reflect your own ideas of its purpose and use.

____

____

____

- Analyse and comment on ideas, methods and approaches used in your own and others' work.

____

____

____

Record of Achievement *I can select and use information to develop my work and evaluate my finished work in a meaningful way.* ☐

Name ______________________ Date ______________

A sense of place

- In class, look at a painting of the environment by a famous artist and then try to copy it.

- What can you see in the painting?

____

- What is the focus of the painting?

____

- Why do you think the artist chose this particular viewpoint?

____

____

- How did the artist use line, colour and pattern in their work?

____

____

____

I can comment on others' work. ☐

Name ______________________ Date ______________

A sense of place

- In the boxes below, draw thumbnail sketches of views that include features you find interesting in the environment and that you may later use in your painting.

- Make notes next to the sketches about interesting patterns, textures and colours that drew your attention.

Record of Achievement

I can collect visual and other information by observing and recording features of the environment. ☐

Name ______________________ Date ______________

A sense of place

- In the frame below, stick a photograph or sketch a picture of the painting you created.

- Evaluate your finished work by answering the following questions:

Why did you select a particular method or approach?

____

____

How did you use the information you collected to inform your work?

____

____

How well do you think you communicated your ideas about the environment in your work?

____

____

I can create a painting based on ideas about the environment and analyse and comment on my finished work. ☐

Name ______________________ Date ______________

Visiting a museum, gallery or site

- Draw a picture of the place you visited, either from the outside or from one of the rooms inside.

The place I visited was called ______________________

- Describe the place you visited and some of the things you did there.

____
____
____

- How did the visit contribute to work you are doing in art and design?

____
____
____

I can describe a place I have visited and explain how the visit has contributed to the work I am doing in class. ☐

Name ________________________ Date ________________

Visiting a museum, gallery or site

- Draw and comment on some of the objects you saw on your visit.

- Comment on how you used some of the information you collected from your visit to help you in your work.

____

____

____

I can comment on a selection of objects I saw on my visit and on how information I collected helped me in my work. ☐

Name ______________________ Date ______________

Visiting a museum, gallery or site

- Draw some objects you saw in the museum and comment on how and why they came to be there.

- Using evidence from your visit comment on how the museum carries out its social, cultural and other functions.

____

____

____

____

Record of Achievement

I can comment on how and why certain objects came to be in the museum I visited and how the museum carries out its social, cultural and other functions. ☐

Music

Music provides the children with opportunities to make and respond to sound and to develop an understanding and appreciation of a wide variety of music. With each of these units, children acquire the knowledge, skills and understanding needed to make music. They also develop interrelated skills of performing, composing and appraising. In particular, in Year 6 they learn how to compose a song, develop their ability to take part in a class performance, and have the opportunity to develop and demonstrate skills and knowledge achieved in previous years.

Due to the musical nature of these units, the photocopiable pages can only be a paper record of the work undertaken by the children.

Songwriter – exploring lyrics and melody
Unit 19

✔ **Learning outcome** (page 109)
To create and perform melodies with help.

✔✔ **Learning outcome** (page 110)
To create a simple song and perform it in a way that reflects its meaning.

✔✔✔ **Learning outcome** (page 111)
To show an understanding of how lyrics can reflect a cultural context and have social meaning.

In following this unit, the children will have developed the ability to compose a song with an awareness of the relationship between lyrics and melody.

When working on this unit, ensure that the children have had an opportunity to use words and phrases related to sounds and structures (*melody, rhythm, phrase, repetition, song structure*); processes (*songwriting, lyrics, attitude*) and context (*social messages*).

The photocopiable pages in this unit require the children to have become familiar with a variety of songs of different styles, to have become aware of simple song structures such as verse/chorus and to have understood the concept of melody. Through this unit, the children learn of the important role played by lyrics in songs, in particular, children look at how lyrics can convey moods or attitudes. Photocopiable page 109 asks the children to draw a picture of themselves performing the melody they created and identify the musical instrument on which they performed their melody. Children completing photocopiable page 110 should be able to write the words of the song they composed, describe the melody to which they put the lyrics and describe how their performance reflected the meaning of their composition. Photocopiable page 111 asks the children to write and illustrate the lyrics from a song they have worked on in class and then describe how they think the lyrics reflect a cultural context and have social meaning.

Stars, hide your fires – performing together

Unit 20

✔ **Learning outcome** (page 112)
To sing with confidence and expression, following the shape of a melody.

✔✔ **Learning outcome** (page 113)
To sing with confidence and expression and play accompaniment parts on chosen instruments.

✔✔✔ **Learning outcome** (page 114)
To sing with confidence the harmony part in a class performance and play the more complex instrumental parts.

In following this unit, the children will have developed their ability to take part in a class performance with confidence, expression and control.

When working on this unit, make sure that the children have had an opportunity to use words and phrases related to sounds (*harmony, rests, timbre, accents);* process (*arranging a given song)* and context *(venue, occasion).*

The photocopiable pages in this unit require the children to have had the opportunity to sing and play a two-part song, play musical accompaniments and rehearse and develop musical and performance ideas, showing an understanding of how to achieve a quality performance. Photocopiable page 112 asks the children to draw a picture of themselves singing during a class performance and then describe the class performance. Children completing photocopiable page 113 should be able to sing confidently and expressively with attention to dynamics and phrasing. They should also be able to play an accompaniment part on a glockenspiel, bass drum or cymbal. They are required to describe their performance and draw a picture of the class performance. Photocopiable page 114 asks the children to describe the instrument they played during a class performance and comment on the notation they used.

Who knows? – Exploring musical processes

Unit 21

✔ **Learning outcome** (page 115)
To create music that meets identified intentions and combines sounds with some awareness of the combined effect.

✔✔ **Learning outcome** (page 116)
To create music that reflects given intentions and uses notations, as a support for creative work and performance.

✔✔✔ **Learning outcome** (page 117)
To take a lead when creating and performing and use a variety of musical devices including melody, rhythms, chords and structures.

In following this unit, the children will have had the opportunity to develop and demonstrate the musical skills, knowledge and understanding achieved in previous years' work.

When working on this unit, ensure that the children have had an opportunity to use words and phrases related to sounds (*pitch, getting higher/lower, duration, longer/shorter, pulse, rhythm, metre, tempo, timbre, texture*); processes (*use of notations, composing, arranging, improvising, performing*) and context (*intentions, purpose, venue, occasion*).

The photocopiable pages in this unit require the children to have had the opportunity to perform rhythmically and with control of pitch, use sounds descriptively in response to different stimuli, listened to and performed a wide range of music and used notations. Photocopiable page 115 asks the children to identify the brief they were given as a stimuli for their musical composition and then asks them to describe their composition. Children completing photocopiable page 116 should be able to describe the brief on which their composition was based and explain how their composition reflects the intentions in their brief. Photocopiable page 117 asks the children to identify how, in their opinion, they took the lead within their group in creating and performing a piece of work and to identify the musical devices they used.

Name ______________________ Date ______________

Songwriter – exploring lyrics and melody

- Draw a picture of you playing the melody you created to an audience of your choice.

- What instrument did you use to perform your melody on? Draw it in the box and write its name here.

____

- Who helped you with your work?

____

____

- Record the notation for your melody in the space provided.

Record of Achievement

I can create and perform melodies with help. ☐

Name ______________________ Date ______________

Songwriter – exploring lyrics and melody

- Write the lyrics to your song.

____

____

____

____

____

____

- Describe the melody of your song.

____

____

____

____

____

- In the box, draw a picture of you performing your song.

- Explain how your performance reflected the meaning of your song.

____

____

____

____

Record of Achievement *I can create my own simple songs and perform them in a way that reflects their meaning.* ☐

Name ______________________ Date ______________

Songwriter – exploring lyrics and melody

- Write the lyrics from a song you have worked on in class and draw pictures to illustrate the words.

- Describe how you think the lyrics reflect cultural context and have social meaning.

____

____

____

____

Record of Achievement

I can show an understanding of how lyrics can reflect a cultural context and have social meaning. ☐

Name ______________________ Date ______________

Stars, hide your fires – performing together

- Draw a picture of you singing in your class performance.

- Describe the class performance.

____

____

____

____

____

Record of Achievement *I can sing confidently and expressively, following the shape of my melody.* ☐

Name ______________________________ Date ____________________

Stars, hide your fires – performing together

- Describe your class performance, identifying the instrument you played and how you felt during the performance.

____

____

____

____

____

- Draw a picture of your class performance

Record of Achievement

I can sing confidently and expressively with attention to dynamics and phrasing and play accompaniment parts on my chosen instrument. ☐

Name ______________________________ Date ____________________

Stars, hide your fires – performing together

- Describe the instrumental part you played in your class performance, identifying your instrument and commenting on the notation you used.

- Draw an accurate picture showing how the children were arranged in the class performance and the instruments they played.

Record of Achievement

I can sing the harmony part in our class performance confidently and accurately and play the more complex instrumental parts. ☐

Name ______________________ Date ______________

Who knows?– Exploring musical processes

- Describe the brief that you used as a stimulus for your composition.

____

____

____

- Using your own symbols as notation, describe your composition, explaining how you combined sounds to create effect.

I can create and perform music that meets intentions and combines sounds with some awareness of the combined effect. ☐

Name ______________________ Date ______________

Who knows?– Exploring musical processes

- Describe the brief on which your composition was based.

____

____

____

____

- Describe your composition explaining how you think it reflects the intentions in your brief.

Record of Achievement

I can create music that reflects given intentions and uses notations as a support for creative work and performance. ☐

Name ______________________________ Date ____________________

Who knows?– Exploring musical processes

- Describe how you think you took the lead in creating and performing within your group.

____

____

____

____

- Describe the musical devices you used in your work.

____

____

____

- Draw a picture of you performing with your group.

Record of Achievement

I can take the lead in creating and performing and can use a variety of musical devices including melody, rhythms, chords and structures. ☐

Design and technology

Design and technology provides children with the opportunity to develop their designing and making skills; improve their knowledge and understanding and capability to create products. They will use their knowledge and understanding of a wide range of materials, components and techniques to design and make quality products. The children are given the opportunity to evaluate their work as it develops and, if necessary, suggest alternatives.

In Year 6, children have the opportunity to work with textiles, a variety of construction materials and components, and sheet materials. The children will apply knowledge and understanding of mechanisms and control systems, structures, existing products, quality and health and safety.

Shelters

Unit 6A

✔ **Learning outcome** (page 123)
To make a simple model shelter incorporating a framework and textile cover.

✔✔ **Learning outcome** (page 124)
To investigate several shelters and construct a model shelter incorporating a framework and a textile cover.

✔✔✔ **Learning outcome** (page 125)
To write a step-by-step approach for making a model shelter.

In this unit, the children learn about structures and how they can fail when loaded. They will have learned the use of certain techniques for reinforcing and strengthening structures.

When working on this unit, make sure the children are familiar with words and phrases related to designing (*modelling, scale, model, fair test*); making (*rolling, strengthening, reinforcing*); knowledge and understanding (*triangulation, diagonal, stable, strength, framework, material, tube, rigid, section, water resistance, strut, beam, bracket, stay member, horizontal, vertical, gusset*) and forces (*tension, compression, bending, twisting*).

The photocopiable pages in this unit require the children to have been shown the strength of tubes as a construction material, and textiles as a suitable cover for a framework. The main outcome of this unit will have been the design and construction of a framework-type shelter for an identified purpose. The photocopiable pages therefore will be used as a record of the practical work undertaken. Photocopiable page 123 asks the children to draw an example of a shelter they have investigated and comment on what they learned about this type of shelter. Children completing photocopiable page 124 should be able to identify three different shelters they have investigated and make an annotated drawing of their finished model. Photocopiable page 125 asks the children to show the annotated design for their shelter. They are asked to write the step-by-step approach to making the model shelter that they followed when making their model.

Slippers

Unit 6B

✔ Learning outcome (page 120)
To gather information to base their work on, and to design and make, with support, a slipper, using textiles.

✔✔ Learning outcome (page 121)
To design and make a slipper and to evaluate the slipper against original specifications.

✔✔✔ Learning outcome (page 122)
To design and make a slipper of

In this unit, children have the opportunity to learn how products (in this case slippers) can be designed for different purposes and people.

When working on this unit,ensure the children are familiar with words and phrases related to designing (*specification, flow chart, mock-up, accurate, users, fabric swatches, working drawing*); making (*pattern/template, working properties*) and knowledge and understanding (*seam, seam allowance, insulation, sole, upper, inner, reinforce, right side/wrong side, stitch, stitching, tacking, wadding, sewing machine, hem*).

The photocopiable pages in this unit require the children to have learned that designers must address a range of needs when designing slippers. They will have learned how to make accurate patterns/templates and detailed working drawings. They will also have developed their making and finishing skills to enhance the quality of their slippers and will have learned how to evaluate their products critically. Photocopiable page 120 asks the children to design a slipper for a child based on the information given on the sheet and to draw a picture or stick a photo of their own textile work that they did in class with the support of an adult. Children completing photocopiable page 121 should be able to list two pieces of information they gathered about slippers and explain how this information influenced their original design. They are then required to draw their finished slipper as a record of the work undertaken, and evaluate their work against their original specification. Photocopiable page 122 asks the children to draw an annotated picture of their finished slipper and describe its construction, appearance and function giving clear reasons for choosing their specific idea.

Fairground

Unit 6C

✔ **Learning outcome** (page 129)
To produce a model with a rotating part.

✔✔ **Learning outcome** (page 130)
To design, make and evaluate a model with a rotating part that is driven by an electric motor.

✔✔✔ **Learning outcome** (page 131)
To analyse possible design ideas in some depth against original design criteria.

In this unit, the children will have gained an understanding of an important mechanism, using belts and pulleys, and have learned more about control, using electricity and an electric motor.

When working on this unit, make sure the children are familiar with words and phrases related to designing (*model, mock-up, select, modify, improvements, design proposal, criteria*); making (*framework, construct, temporary joins, permanent pins*) and knowledge and understanding (*rotation, spindle, axle, drive belt, pulley, electric motor, speed, framework, horizontal, vertical, electric circuit, switch, gearing up or down, computer control, mechanism*).

The photocopiable pages in this unit require the children to have been introduced to computer control. The photocopiable pages for this unit will be used as a record of the practical work undertaken by the children. Photocopiable page 129 asks the children to draw a picture or stick a photo of their completed model. They are also asked to draw a diagram of the rotating part and describe how it works. Children completing photocopiable page 130 should have made a model with a rotating part that is driven by an electric motor. The photocopiable asks them to record their design and the design criteria they used. Having made the model, they are then asked to evaluate it against the design criteria. Photocopiable page 131 requires the children to identify their design criteria and to draw two of their possible design ideas for their model. Finally, they are asked to analyse their design ideas against their design criteria.

Controllable vehicles

Unit 6D

✔ **Learning outcome** (page 132)
To construct, with support, a basic model that incorporates a motor.

✔✔ **Learning outcome** (page 133)
To understand how electricity can be used to drive products and design and make a working toy vehicle.

✔✔✔ **Learning outcome** (page 134)
To design and produce a quality product that is appropriate for its user and to evaluate their work

In following this unit the children will have developed their understanding of how products can be driven by electricity. They will have learned how to use motors within their models and how to control the speed and direction of movement.

When working on this unit make sure the children are familiar with words and phrases related to designing (*design proposal, criteria, exploded diagrams, labelled drawings, improvements, construction kits, modify);* making *(cutting jig, cladding, finishing technique, assembling, components)* and knowledge and understanding *(circuit, – both series and parallel – control, motor, chassis, secure connections, switch/short circuit, pressure switch, speed, motor spindle, pulley, wheel, axle, motor mounting clip).*

The photocopiable pages in this unit require the children to have developed their designing skills by using their own ideas and experiences to produce clearly labelled drawings. Photocopiable page 132 asks the children to draw a diagram of the design they used to make a basic model that incorporates a motor. Children completing photocopiable page 133 should have looked at different ways in which electricity can be used to drive products. Photocopiable page 134 asks the children to draw a labelled diagram describing how their toy was constructed and identify the main stages of construction. They are then asked to describe ways in which they could have improved their model.

Name ______________________________ Date ________________

Shelters

- Draw and label an example of a shelter that you have investigated in class.

- What did you learn from looking at this type of shelter?

____

____

- Reproduce below the annotated design you used for your model shelter.

Record of Achievement *I can make a simple model shelter incorporating a framework and a textile cover.* ☐

Name ______________________ Date ______________

Shelters

- Draw and label three different types of shelter that you have investigated.

______________ ______________ ______________

- What did you learn from your investigations?

____

____

- Draw and annotate a picture of your finished model shelter.

I can investigate several shelters and make a model shelter incorporating a framework and a textile cover. ☐

Name ______________________ Date ______________

Shelters

- Draw an annotated design for your model shelter, listing the materials to be used and the methods of construction.

- Set out the step-by-step order you would follow to construct your shelter.

- ______________________
- ______________________
- ______________________
- ______________________
- ______________________
- ______________________
- ______________________
- ______________________

Record of Achievement *I can set out a step-by-step approach to how my shelter will be made.* ☐

Name ______________________________ Date __________________

Slippers

Rachael and James are both 11 years of age and each need a new pair of slippers. Rachael's favourite colour is blue. James is mad about football.

- Pick one of the children and design a suitable pair of slippers for her or him.

These slippers are for ________________

- In the space below, draw a picture or stick a photograph of the slippers you made in class.

I can gather information to base my work on and with support design and make a slipper. ☐

Name ______________________________ Date ________________

Slippers

- List two pieces of information you gained from your investigation of different types of slippers.

1. ____

2. ____

- How did this information influence your own design for a slipper?

____

____

- Draw a picture of your finished slipper and evaluate it against your original specification.

____

____

____

____

Record of Achievement

I can use information I have gathered to inform my design for a slipper and then make a slipper which I can evaluate against the original specification. ☐

Name ______________________ Date ______________

Slippers

- Draw an annotated picture of your finished slipper.

- Describe your slipper explaining your reasons for your choice of design, the methods you used when constructing it, and its appearance and function.

- Describe any changes you made to your design as it developed.

Record of Achievement *I can work independently to design and make a slipper of high quality, evaluating my finished work.* ☐

Name ______________________ Date ______________

Fairground

- In the space below, draw a picture or stick a photograph of your finished model.

- Draw in detail the rotating part of your model and describe how it works.

Record of Achievement

I can produce a model with a rotating part. ☐

Name ______________________ Date ______________

Fairground

- Show your design for your model.

My design criteria were: ______________________

Evaluation of my model against my design criteria: ______________________

- Describe any modifications you made to your model as you made it.

Record of Achievement *I can design, make, evaluate and modify a model with a rotating part that is driven by an electric motor.* ☐

Name ______________________ Date ______________

Fairground

- What were your design criteria for your model?

____

____

____

____

- Show two possible design ideas for your model.

- Analyse these design ideas against your design criteria.

____

____

____

____

____

Record of Achievement

I can analyse possible design ideas for my model against my design criteria. ☐

Name ______________________________ Date ____________________

Controllable vehicles

- Draw a diagram of your design for the model you made.

- Describe how you used electricity to drive the motor in your model.

Record of Achievement

I can, with support, construct a basic model that incorporates a motor. ☐

Name ______________________________ Date ____________________

Controllable vehicles

- Draw two labelled diagrams to show different ways in which electricity can be used to drive products.

- Draw a picture of your finished working toy vehicle.

I can understand how electricity is used to drive products and have designed and made a working toy vehicle. ☐

Name ______________________ Date ______________

Controllable vehicles

- Describe who your toy was designed for and how this influenced your design.

____

____

____

- Make a labelled diagram to show how you constructed your model and identify the main stages of making.

- How do you think you could have improved your model?

____

____

____

Record of Achievement

I can design and produce a quality product having considered the user of the toy in my design and identified what could be done to improve my work. ☐

Religious education

Religious education provides children with the opportunity to develop their skills in working with others and treating others with respect. It allows them to consider their own experiences, attitudes and values, and those of other people. In listening to stories, children will develop their understanding about beliefs and cultures of others; the importance of sharing celebration and festivals and learn about a variety of cultural and religious traditions.

In Year 6, children will have the opportunity to study the worship of several religions, learn about the mosque and its role in the Muslim community, deepen their understanding and knowledge of the Qu'ran and find out about the importance and significance of sacred texts to believers. They will also have the opportunity to understand how religious buildings exemplify the beliefs and values of religious communities and to focus on some of the ways in which music, art and drama are used to express aspects of faith.

Worship and community – generic
Unit 6A

✔ **Learning outcome** (page 142)
To identify and describe acts of worship using technical vocabulary.

✔✔ **Learning outcome** (page 143)
To compare acts of worship in two different religions.

✔✔✔ **Learning outcome** (page 144)
To describe some of the responsibilities and benefits of belonging to a religious community.

This unit gives the children the opportunity to study several religions, looking at the key features of worship and what worship means to a believer.

When working on this unit, make sure the children are familiar with words and phrases related to worship in the faith community being studied (*communion, prayer, meditation, salah, muezzin, arti, puja*) and formal prayers (using simplified language without changing the meaning).

In this unit, the children will have explored the ways different faith groups use prayer as part of their worship. By using written and visual resources and by meeting faith adherents, they will have learned about the importance of community and the responsibilities that a religious community has about the way they live in the wider world. Photocopiable page 142 asks the children to explain in their own words what is meant by the term worship and to identify the religion they studied in class. They are then required to choose three different aspects of worship and explain why they are carried out by the religion they have studied. Children completing photocopiable page 143 should be able to identify the two religions they studied, draw and label an artefact from each religion explaining its role/meaning in an act of worship, and describe similarities and differences in acts of worship carried out by believers. Photocopiable page 144 asks the children to identify some of the responsibilities and benefits that come with belonging to a religious community.

Worship and community – what is the role of the mosque?

Unit 6B

✓ Learning outcome (page 145)
To describe a mosque using some correct terms, and explain what it is used for.

✓✓ Learning outcome (page 146)
To identify some key Islamic beliefs using technical terms, and show an understanding of how these are expressed in worship in a mosque.

✓✓✓ Learning outcome (page 147)
To identify similarities between Islamic beliefs and practices and other religions studied.

In following this unit, the children will have learned about the mosque and the role it plays in the Muslim community, reflecting on what is involved in belonging to a community.

When working on this unit, make sure the children are familiar with words and phrases related to Islam (*mosque, minaret, Allah, Makkah)* religious beliefs (*respect, sacred*) and worship (*prayer*).

The photocopiable pages in this unit require the children to have developed their understanding of how religious beliefs are expressed in practice, by studying how worship takes place in the mosque. They will have built on earlier work on religious experiences and expression, and on previous experiences of visiting religious buildings. Photocopiable page 145 asks the children to draw a picture of a mosque and describe what one is like. This description should include a mention of the art found on both the outside and inside of a mosque, and an explanation of why there are no human or animal representations. Children completing photocopiable page 146 should be able to identify the correct terms of some key Islamic beliefs and explain how they are expressed in worship in a Mosque. Photocopiable page 147 asks the children to identify some similarities between Islamic beliefs and practices and other religions they have studied.

Why are sacred texts important? – Generic

Unit 6C

✔ **Learning outcome** (page 148)
To name a sacred text and explain its treatment by believers.

✔✔ **Learning outcome** (page 149)
To describe how sacred texts are treated and explain a main message from a sacred text.

✔✔✔ **Learning outcome** (page 150)
To explain how a person of a particular faith group may act when faced with a certain dilemma, using quotes from a sacred text to illustrate their answer.

In following this unit, children will find out about the importance and significance of sacred texts to believers.

When working on this unit, make sure that the children are familiar with words and phrases related to the treatment of sacred texts (*romallas, chauri, scroll, Ark*); the content of sacred texts (*gospel, psalm, prophecy, Hadith, laws*) and the names of sacred texts (*Guru Granth Sahib, Qur'an, Vedas, Bible, Torah*).

The photocopiable pages in this unit require the children to have used a sacred text from a specific religion, and will therefore be generic in order to make them suitable for the study of different texts. It is assumed that the children will have used a variety of sources. They will have used material taken directly from their chosen sacred text and studied its meaning and effect on the lives of believers. Photocopiable page 148 asks the children to identify the sacred text they have studied and explain how it is treated by believers. Photocopiable page 149 asks the children to name two sacred texts and then compare how and why these texts are treated in special ways. They are also required to explain one of the main messages of the sacred text they have studied. Photocopiable page 150 asks the children describe an imaginary situation in which a character uses their knowledge of their particular sacred text to help them solve a personal dilemma, giving a direct quote to help illustrate their answer.

What is the Qur'an and why is it important to Muslims?

Unit 6D

✓ **Learning outcome** (page 151)
To know how Muslims treat the Qur'an and how their lives are affected by its teachings.

✓✓ **Learning outcome** (page 152)
To identify a main message from the Qur'an and explain why the Qu'ran is treated in a special way.

✓✓✓ **Learning outcome** (page 153)
To form questions about the effect of the Qur'an on Muslims' lives.

In this unit, the children will have deepened their knowledge and understanding of the Qur'an and appreciated its significance for Muslims. This unit builds on work done for other units on Islam, namely Units 5A and 5B.

When working on this unit make sure the children are familiar with words and phrases related to Islam (*Qur'an, Hafiz, Bismillah, Madrasah*) and religion (*blasphemy, sacred, mystery, revelation, authority, reverence, compassionate, merciful*).

The photocopiable pages in this unit require the children to have studied sacred texts in other religions and so understand concepts such as 'word of God' and 'holy'. They should also have an understanding of some important Muslim beliefs. They should have visited a mosque and seen, in the place of worship, the sacred text being read. Photocopiable page 151 asks the children to describe ways that Muslims treat the Qur'an in order to show that it is special. They should also be able to describe how a Muslim's life might be affected by a teaching from the Qur'an. Children completing photocopiable page 152 should be able to describe a main message of the Qur'an, and explain what this means. Photocopiable page 153 asks the children to write four questions they could ask Muslims about the effect of the Qur'an on their lives.

What can we learn from Christian religious buildings?

Unit 6E

✔ **Learning outcome** (page 154)
To identify parts of Christian religious buildings and religious objects and say why they have value for members of religious communities.

✔✔ **Learning outcome** (page 155)
To describe the interior and exterior of a Christian religious building, identify key features and explain how they are used in worship.

✔✔✔ **Learning outcome** (page 156)
To explain hpw the key feature of two contrasting religious buildings relate to different Christian traditions, beliefs and forms of worship.

In following this unit, the children will have learned how religious buildings exemplify the beliefs and values of religious communities. This unit builds on work that children will have done on Christian beliefs, the Key Stage 1 unit on a visit to a church and the Key Stage 2 unit on signs and symbols.

When working on this unit, make sure the children are familiar with words and phrases related to Christian buildings (*font, altar, pulpit, vestry, ecumenical*) and words describing meanings beyond the literal (*'It is like', 'sounds like', 'bit like', awesome, mystery*).

The photocopiable pages in this unit require the children to have studied two Christian denominations to deepen their knowledge, and to have explored how signs, symbols, and metaphors are used to extend and deepen religious understanding. Photocopiable page 154 asks the children identify illustrations of key features found in Christian religious buildings and explain why they have value for the members of that religious community. Children completing photocopiable page 155 should be able to identify three key features (interior and exterior) in a religious building, for example font, altar, pulpit, vestry, and explain how they are used in worship. Photocopiable page 156 asks the children to identify two different religious buildings and contrast a key feature found in both buildings.

How do people express their faith through the arts?

Unit 6F

✔ **Learning outcome** (page 157)
To understand that music, art and drama can be used to express faith.

✔✔ **Learning outcome** (page 158)
To understand that expressing faith can involve feelings and emotions and that religious beliefs can be expressed through creative and expressive arts.

✔✔✔ **Learning outcome** (page 159)
To recognise and express feelings in response to ways in which religious experience is represented through the arts.

In following this unit, the children will have focused on some of the ways in which music, art and drama are used to express aspects of faith.

When working on this unit, make sure that the children are familiar with words and phrases related to Christianity (*vestments, stained glass, icons, festival, service, miracle plays, Pentecost*) and Islam (*prayer mat, mosque, mosaic, calligraphy, Arabesque*)

The photocopiable pages in this unit require the children to have focused on Christianity and Islam with reference to Hinduism. The unit will have provided opportunities for children to experience how certain art forms can be used to express feelings, emotions and intentions and children will have learned how these can be used in a religious context to express faith. Photocopiable page 157 asks the children to draw specific pictures representing music, art and drama and explain how the examples drawn are used in some religions as a way of expressing faith. For photocopiable page 158, children are required to draw a copy of a religious painting they have looked at in class. The children are then asked to describe what religious belief they think the artist was trying to show in the painting. Children completing photocopiable page 159 should be able to design a stained glass window that illustrates a religious belief and describe how they hope it would make people feel if they saw it in a religious building.

Name ______________________ Date ______________

Worship and community – generic

- Explain what is meant by the word **worship**.

____

____

____

- Identify the religion you studied in class. ______________

- Choose **three** different aspects of worship from the religion you studied. Explain why these aspects of worship are carried out. Draw pictures to help illustrate your answers.

Record of Achievement

I can identify and describe some aspects of worship using technical vocabulary. ☐

Name ______________________ Date ______________

Worship and community – generic

- Name the two religions you have chosen to compare.

1. ______________________

2. ______________________

- Draw and label one artefact from each of the above religions and describe its role/meaning in an act of worship.

- Describe one similarity and one difference in the acts of worship carried out by believers of these religions.

Similarity	Difference

Record of Achievement *I can compare worship in one religion with worship in a second religion that I have also studied at this Key Stage.* ☐

Name ________________________ Date ________________

Worship and community – generic

Record of Achievement *I can explain some of the responsibilities and benefits of being part of a religious community.* ☐

Name ______________________ Date ______________

Worship and community – what is the role of the mosque?

- Draw a picture of a mosque that has a minaret.
- Label the **dome** and the **minaret**.
- Describe a mosque.

____

____

____

____

____

____

- Describe the functions of the following places found in a mosque.

Mihrab

____

____

Minbar

____

____

Minaret

____

____

Record of Achievement *I can describe a mosque using some correct terms, and explain what it is used for.* ☐

Name ______________________________ Date ____________________

Worship and community – what is the role of the mosque?

- Explain what the following terms mean to a Muslim and how they are expressed in worship.

Salah means	Makkah is
The Ka'ba is	The Hajj is
Ramadan is	Muhammad was

I can use correct terms to describe some of the key beliefs of Islam and show an understanding of how these are expressed in worship in a mosque. ☐

Name ______________________ Date ______________

Worship and community – what is the role of the mosque?

- In the table below, list some similarities between Islamic beliefs and practices and other religions you have studied.

Islamic belief/practice	Similar belief/practice in another religion

Record of Achievement *I can identify some similarities between Islamic beliefs and practices and those of other religions I have studied.* ☐

Name ______________________ Date ______________

Why are sacred texts important?

The sacred text I have studied is: ______________________

- Explain how the text is treated by believers and draw a picture to illustrate your answer.

____

____

____

____

____

____

____

Record of Achievement

I can name a sacred text and explain how it should be treated. ☐

Name ______________________ Date ______________

Why are sacred texts important?

- Name two sacred texts

1. ____

2. ____

- Describe and compare **how** and **why** these texts are treated in special ways

Text 1

____

____

____

____

Text 2

____

____

____

____

- Explain the main messages of the sacred text you have studied.

____

____

____

____

____

Record of Achievement

I can describe and compare how and why texts are treated in special ways and explain one of the main messages of the sacred text I have studied. ☐

Name ______________________ Date ______________

Why are sacred texts important?

- Draw a picture of the imaginary person you will use in your work, identifying their faith group.

- Describe a dilemma your character finds him/herself in.

____
____
____
____
____
____
____

- Explain how they could use the sacred text of their faith to help them find a solution to their dilemma.

____
____
____
____
____
____

- Identify a direct quote from the sacred text to illustrate your answer.

____
____

Record of Achievement

I can explain how a person of a particular faith group may act when faced with a certain dilemma, using quotes from a sacred text in my explanation. ☐

Name ______________________ Date ______________

What is the Qur'an and why is it important to Muslims?

- What do Muslims use as their holy book? ______________________

- Describe three ways in which Muslims treat the Qur'an to show that it is special to them. Illustrate your answers.

- Describe how a Muslim's life might be affected by a teaching from the Qur'an.

Record of Achievement

I can describe how a Qur'an would be treated by a Muslim and how a Muslim's life might be affected by a teaching from the Qur'an. ☐

Name ______________________________ Date __________________

What is the Qur'an and why is it important to Muslims?

- Identify one of the main messages of the Qur'an.

____

____

- Explain what it means.

____

____

- The Qur'an is treated in a special way by Muslims. Draw three pictures that illustrate the different ways in which Muslims show it is special.

I can describe and explain one of the main messages of the Qur'an and how and why it is treated in a special way by Muslims. ☐

Name ______________________ Date ______________

What is the Qur'an and why is it important to Muslims?

- Compose four questions you could ask Muslims about how their lives are affected by the Qu'ran. Write the questions in the speech bubbles.

Record of Achievement *I can form questions to ask Muslims about the effect of the Qur'an on their lives.* ☐

Name ______________________ Date ______________

What can we learn from Christian religious buildings?

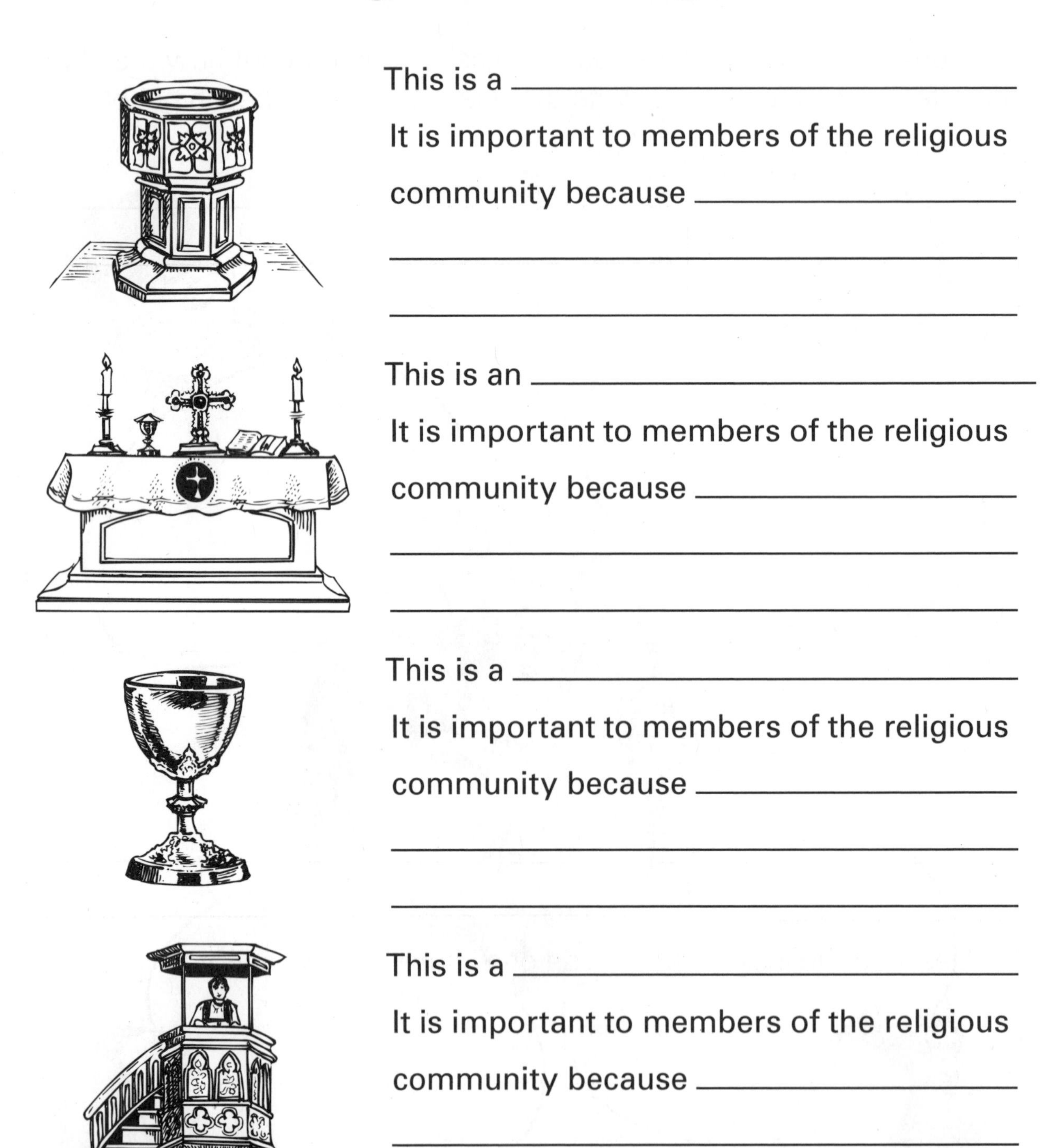

This is a ______________________

It is important to members of the religious community because ______________________

____

____

This is an ______________________

It is important to members of the religious community because ______________________

____

____

This is a ______________________

It is important to members of the religious community because ______________________

____

____

This is a ______________________

It is important to members of the religious community because ______________________

____

____

Record of Achievement

I can name some parts of Christian religious buildings and religious objects and say why they have value for members of religious communities. ☐

Name ______________________ Date ______________

What can we learn from Christian religious buildings?

- Draw and label three key features that you could find in a religious building and explain how they are used in worship.

- Describe the inside and outside of a church you have visited.

Record of Achievement

I can describe the interior and exterior of a Christian religious building, identify key features and explain how they are used in worship. ☐

Name ______________________ Date ______________

What can we learn from Christian religious buildings?

- Identify two religious buildings from different Christian traditions.

____

____

- Draw two contrasting features found in the buildings named above.

- Explain how these features relate to the different Christian traditions, beliefs and forms of worship.

____

____

____

____

Record of Achievement

I can explain how the key features of two contrasting religious buildings relate to different Christian traditions, beliefs and forms of worship. ☐

Name ______________________________ Date ________________

How do people express their faith through the arts?

- Draw a picture of people singing in church.

- Why do you think people sing hymns and listen to music in church?

____

____

____

- Draw an example of Islamic art.

- How do Muslims use art to express their faith?

____

____

____

____

____

- Draw Rama and Sita.

- How do Hindus use drama to express their faith?

____

____

____

____

____

Record of Achievement

I can understand that music, art and drama are used in some religions as a means of expressing faith. ☐

Name ______________________ Date ______________

How do people express their faith through the arts?

- Draw a copy of a religious painting you have looked at in class.

- What religious belief do you think the artist was trying to show in this painting?

____

____

- How do you think people feel when they look at this artwork?

____

____

____

Record of Achievement

I can understand that expressing faith can involve feelings and emotions and that religious beliefs can be expressed through creative and expressive arts. ☐

Name ______________________________ Date ________________

How do people express their faith through the arts?

- Design a stained glass window to illustrate a religious belief. Draw your design below.

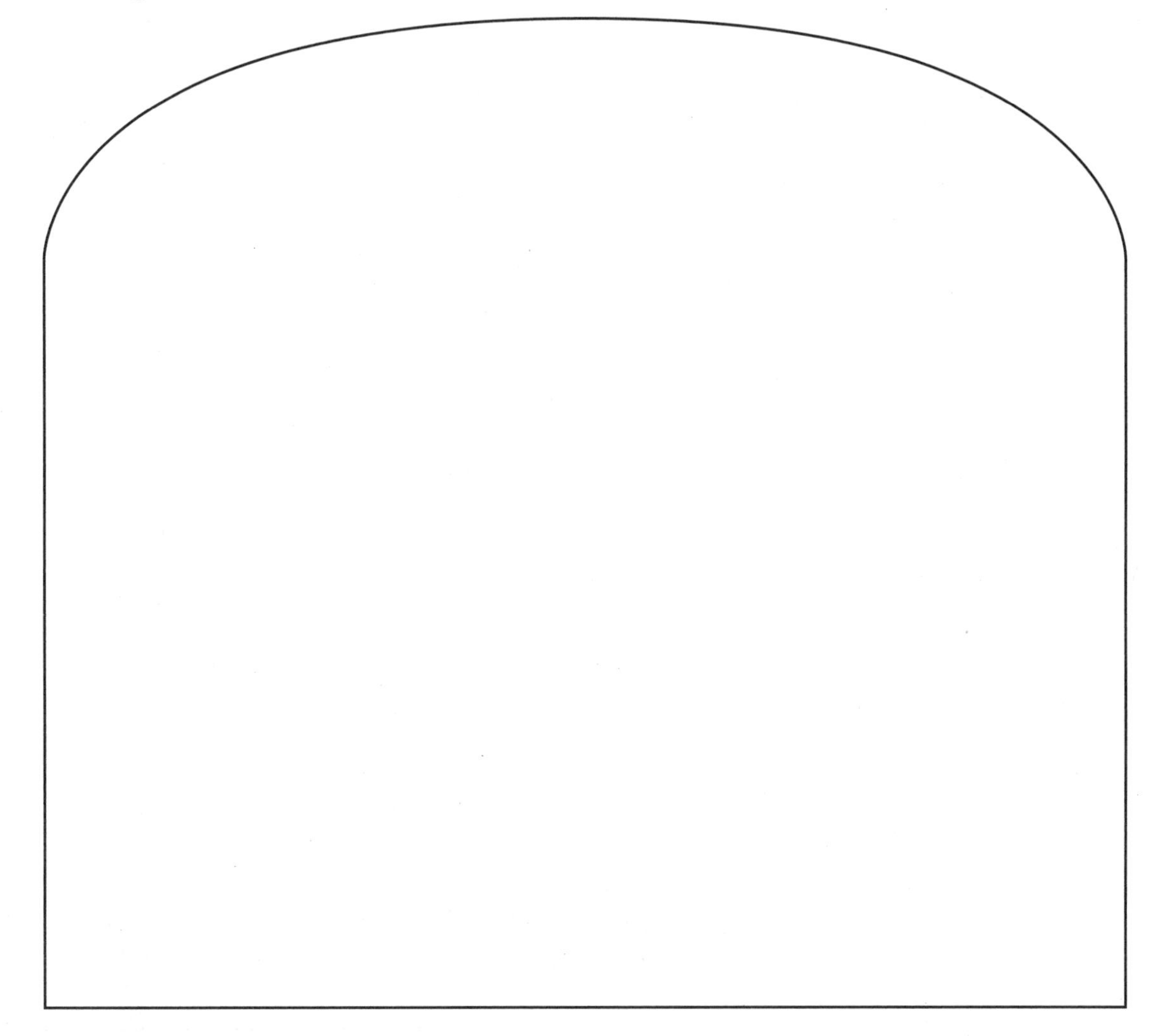

- How do you think people would feel if they saw this window in a religious building?

____

____

____

I can recognise and express feelings in response to ways in which religious experience is represented through the arts. ☐

PSHE and citizenship

This section is based on the non-statutory guidelines for PSHE and the QCA documents for citizenship in the National Curriculum at Key Stage 2.

In Year 6, the children will express how they feel about the changes that are happening to their bodies and feelings; they will discuss concerns they have and they will consider the impact illegal drugs can have on them and others.

The citizenship worksheets are based on the QCA Scheme of Work for citizenship. In Year 6, the children can study Unit 11, 'In the media – what's in the news' (researching the different types of media that give us news and information) and Unit 12, 'Moving on' (considering what it will be like to move to Key Stage 3).

Changes

✓ **Learning outcomes** (page 165)
To identify some changes that are happening to their bodies. To be able to say how they feel about the changes.

✓✓ **Learning outcomes** (page 166)
To describe some changes that take place at the time of puberty. To recognise that these changes can cause people to worry.

✓✓✓ **Learning outcomes** (page 167)
To identify some good and not so good things about growing up. To recognise that it is important not to rush into growing up.

In this section, the children will be discussing the changes that are taking place in their bodies and how this affects their feelings and emotions. This is a sensitive issue and the level of detail that is covered will depend on the policy for sex education that is adhered to in individual schools. As there is a difference in the age that children reach puberty, this also needs to be considered. In light of this, the photocopiable pages have been designed to be used at any level.

When working on this unit, make sure that the children have become familiar with words and phrases relating to changes (*change, body, feelings, emotions, growing up, worried, concerned, developing, puberty*).

Photocopiable page 165 requires the children to explain how they know that their body is changing and describe how they feel about these changes. Children completing photocopiable page 166 are asked to describe some ways in which their bodies and feelings are changing. They are required to explain some things people might worry about regarding these changes. For photocopiable page 167, children have to describe how they feel about the changes taking place to their bodies. They are also required to explain some of the good and not so good things about growing up and why it is important not to rush growing up.

Dangers of drugs

✔ **Learning outcome** (page 168)
To recognise some of the effects of illegal drugs.

✔✔ **Learning outcome** (page 169)
To recognise that illegal drugs can be dangerous and understand how to avoid becoming involved in them.

✔✔✔ **Learning outcomes** (page 170)
To recognise the pressures that can be put on people to take illegal drugs. To suggest ways people can avoid illegal drugs.

In this section the children will consider the dangers of illegal drugs. They will find out about the harm drugs can do to the human body, feelings and relationships and so on. This subject will need to be handled very sensitively and will depend on the background and home lives of the children. The children will need to consider how others might put pressure on people to take illegal drugs and suggest ways to avoid these pressures themselves and help other people. It may be advisable to bring someone into school to talk about this subject.

When working on this unit make sure the children have become familiar with words and phrases relating to drugs (*risk, expensive, crime, persuade, involved, hooked, family, friends, ill, die, addicted, dangerous, illegal, affect*).

Photocopiable page 168 requires the children to explain what is meant by an illegal drug and give some reasons for not taking them. Children completing photocopiable page 169 are asked to read some untrue statements about taking drugs and explain how they know they are untrue. They are also required to suggest two ways to avoid being persuaded to take illegal drugs. For photocopiable page 170 children have to consider the case of a girl who has got involved in taking illegal drugs and explain some of the pressures that might have forced her into this situation. They are required to suggest some ways they could help her.

In the media – what's in the news?

Unit 11

✔ **Learning outcomes** (page 171)
To identify some different types of media. To understand the media have a role to play in getting news and information to the public.

✔✔ **Learning outcomes** (page 172)
To name some different types of media. To recognise that stories can be presented differently in different media.

✔✔✔ **Learning outcomes** (page 173)
To know that different media present news and information in different ways. To understand that different people may hold different points of view.

In this unit, the children learn about the role of the media (local and national) in communicating news and information to the public. The children will have opportunities to develop skills of enquiry and communication as they discuss and analyse a variety of media. They will discuss issues of topical and personal interest in the local or national news, and compare the different ways that a news story is presented in different publications.

When working on this unit, make sure that the children have become familiar with words and phrases relating to news (*news story, article, feature, report, bias, balance, influence, information*) and media (*television, radio, cinema, newspaper, magazine, popular music, Internet*).

Photocopiable page 171 requires the children to identify different types of media from a given list and then to choose one of them and explain how it supplies news and information to the public. Children completing photocopiable page 172 are required to list as many different types of media as they can. They are then required to explain how an article about something on television might differ from an article written in a newspaper. For example, on television there can be up-to-date moving pictures with a reporter live at the scene, whereas in a newspaper the photographs will have been taken some time previously. For photocopiable page 173, children have to complete a table showing the different ways three types of media can present information. They are also required to explain how there might be differing views from different people about an issue in school and to express their own opinion.

Moving on
Unit 12

✔ **Learning outcomes** (page 174)
To be able to express feelings about moving to Key Stage 3. To recall some information about their new school.

✔✔ **Learning outcomes** (page 175)
To understand what to expect in the move to Key Stage 3. To recognise that change can be good or bad and that change takes place at other times in our lives.

✔✔✔ **Learning outcomes** (page 176)
To understand how others might feel about moving to Key Stage 3. To recognise change can affect different people in different ways and that preparation can help people manage change.

In this unit, the children will consider preparing for the move to Key Stage 3 and a new school by exploring feelings associated with change and transition. They will consider the idea of the school as a community and develop strategies that enable them to manage the change more effectively.

When working on this unit make sure the children have become familiar with words and phrases relating to transition (*change, transfer, confidence, decision-making, discussion*).

Photocopiable page 174 requires the children to describe some of the good feelings they have about moving to Key Stage 3. They are also asked to describe some of their concerns and list three things they know about their new school. Children completing photocopiable page 175 should be able to write about something they expect to happen when they move to Key Stage 3 and describe how changing to Key Stage 3 can be a good and/or bad experience. For photocopiable page 176 children have to describe three different people's feelings about moving to Key Stage 3. They are also required to describe how two people who are both worried about the move to Key Stage 3 might react differently and to list ways they could prepare for the move.

Name ______________________ Date ________________

Changes

- How do you know your body is growing and changing?

____

- How do you feel about your body growing and changing?

____

Record of Achievement

I understand that my body is growing and changing.
I can express how I feel about these changes. ☐

Name ______________________________ Date ____________________

Changes

- Describe some ways your body is growing and changing.

____
____
____
____
____
____
____

- Describe how your feelings are changing.

____
____
____
____
____

- Some people can become very worried about these changes. Explain some of the things they might worry about.

____
____
____
____

Record of Achievement

I can describe some changes to my body and the way I feel. I understand that these changes can cause people to worry. ☐

Name ______________________ Date ______________

Changes

- What are the good things about growing up?

- What are the not so good things about growing up?

- Why do you think it is important not to rush into growing up?

Record of Achievement

I can identify some good and not so good things about growing up. I recognise that it is important not to rush into growing up. ☐

Name ______________________ Date ______________

Dangers of drugs

- Explain what is meant by the term **illegal drugs**.

- Give at least two reasons for not taking illegal drugs

1. ______________________

2. ______________________

Record of Achievement

I can recognise some of the effects of illegal drugs. ☐

Name ______________________________ Date ____________________

Dangers of drugs

- Read the following statements and explain how you know they are untrue.

If I take illegal drugs, it will not damage my health.

____

____

____

If I take illegal drugs, I will be able to stop at any time.

____

____

____

If I take illegal drugs, it will not affect my family.

____

____

____

- Suggest two ways you could avoid being persuaded to take illegal drugs.

1. ____

____

____

2. ____

____

____

Record of Achievement *I recognise that illegal drugs can be harmful to me and understand how to avoid becoming involved in them.* ☐

Name ______________________ Date ______________

Dangers of drugs

Emma is a quiet girl who doesn't have many friends. She has become involved with a group at school and has started taking illegal drugs – a situation she is not very happy about.

- Explain some of the pressures that might have been responsible for Emma getting into this situation.

____

____

____

____

____

- Suggest some ways you could help Emma.

____

____

____

____

____

____

____

Record of Achievement

I understand pressure can be put on people to take illegal drugs and can suggest ways they can avoid them. ☐

Name ______________________________ Date ____________________

In the media – what's in the news?

- Put circles round the things below that are part of the media.

television shops radio banks

newspapers restaurants

Internet schools film

- Choose one of the above that you have circled:

____

- Explain how it supplies information to the public.

____

____

____

____

____

____

____

____

____

Record of Achievement

I can identify some different types of media. I realise the media have a role to play in getting news and information to the public. ☐

Name ______________________________ Date ____________________

In the media – what's in the news?

- List as many different types of media as you can.

______________________________ ______________________________

______________________________ ______________________________

______________________________ ______________________________

______________________________ ______________________________

- Explain how a news article on television might be different from a news article in a newspaper.

____

____

____

____

____

____

____

____

____

____

____

____

____

____

____

I can name different types of media. I can recognise that stories can be presented differently in different media. ☐

Name ______________________________ Date ________________

In the media – what's in the news?

● There are lots of different ways of presenting information. They include: **video pictures; written information; photographs; maps; diagrams; sound recordings and interviews**. In the table below, list the ways of presenting information for three types of media. Some might fit into more than one category.

Television	Radio	Newspaper

● Imagine you were writing an article on homework. Explain two differing views you might be given, who would give them and why.

1. ____

____

____

2. ____

____

____

● What is your own view and why do you think this?

____

____

____

Record of Achievement *I know that different media present news and information in different ways. I understand that different people may hold different points of view.* ☐

Name ______________________ Date ______________

Moving on

- Describe some of the good feelings you have about moving to Key Stage 3.

___

___

___

___

- Describe some of the concerns you have about moving to Key Stage 3.

___

___

___

___

- Write three things you have found out about your new school.

1. ___

___

___

2. ___

___

___

3. ___

___

___

Record of Achievement

I can express my feelings about moving to Key Stage 3.
I know some information about my new school. ☐

Name ______________________ Date ______________

Moving on

- Write about something you expect to happen when you move to Key Stage 3.

____

____

____

- How can changing to Key Stage 3 be a good experience?

____

____

____

- How can changing to Key Stage 3 be a bad experience?

____

____

____

- Describe three other changes that could take place in your life around this time.

1. ____

____

2. ____

____

3. ____

____

Record of Achievement

I know some things to expect when I move to Key Stage 3. I recognise that change can be good or bad. I know that change takes place at other times in my life. ☐

Name ______________________ Date ______________

Moving on

- Write about three different people who each feel differently about moving to Key Stage 3.

1. ______________________________

2. ______________________________

3. ______________________________

- Describe how two people who are both worried about moving to Key Stage 3 might react differently.

1. ______________________________

____

2. ______________________________

____

- List three ways you could prepare for the move to Key Stage 3.

1. ______________________________

2. ______________________________

3. ______________________________

- Describe how this will help you manage better.

____

____

____

____

Record of Achievement

I can understand about how others might feel about moving to Key Stage 3. I recognise change can affect different people in different ways and that preparation can help people manage change. ☐